The Stress Factor in Dogs

Unlocking Resiliency and Enhancing Well-Being

Kristina Spaulding, PhD, CAAB

Wenatchee, Washington U.S.A.

The Stress Factor in Dogs
Unlocking Resiliency and Enhancing Well-Being
Kristina Spaulding, PhD, CAAB

Dogwise Publishing
A Division of Direct Book Service, Inc.
403 South Mission Street, Wenatchee, Washington 98801
1-509-663-9115, 1-800-776-2665
www.dogwisepublishing.com / info@dogwisepublishing.com

Art director: Jon Luke
Interior: Lindsay Davisson
Cover design: Jesús Cordero

Library of Congress Cataloging-in-Publication Data

Names: Spaulding, Kristina, 1977- author. Title: The stress factor in dogs : unlocking resiliency and enhancing well-being / Kristina Spaulding, PhD, CAAB. Description: Wenatchee, Washington: Dogwise Publishing, [2022] | Includes bibliographical references and index. Identifiers: LCCN 2022006068 (print) | LCCN 2022006069 (ebook) | ISBN 9781617813184 (paperback) | ISBN 9781617813191 (ebook) Subjects: LCSH: Dogs--Psychology. | Dogs--Behavior. | Stress (Psychology) Classification: LCC SF433 .S64 2022 (print) | LCC SF433 (ebook) | DDC 636.7--dc23/eng/20220322 LC record available at https://lccn.loc.gov/2022006068 LC ebook record available at https://lccn.loc.gov/2022006069

ISBN: 9781617813184 Printed in the U.S.A.

Dedication

To my father, John Spaulding, for inspiring my deep love of science and learning and showing me how to live life with love, compassion and integrity.

Table of Contents

Acknowledgments

I have many people to thank for helping me make this book possible.

A huge heartfelt thank you to Veronica Boutelle and Gina Phairas at dogbiz for your guidance over more than a decade. There is absolutely no doubt in my mind that I would not be where I am today if it weren't for your support and advice. Thank you for having faith in me—over and over again—when I didn't have faith in myself and for providing me with ethical and effective business assistance. You've made a huge difference for me, personally, and for our profession as a whole and we all owe you a huge debt of gratitude.

A big thank you to Patricia McConnell for taking the time to meet with me on multiple occasions as an undergraduate and for guiding me through the process of becoming a Certified Applied Animal Behaviorist. And then again for taking time out of your extremely busy schedule to provide invaluable feedback on the manuscript itself. This book would have been far more technical and less accessible if it weren't for her insightful input.

Thank you to both Irith Bloom and Crista Coppola for providing feedback on my early drafts and for giving me the confidence to submit them to the publisher. I am also grateful for the patience and kind support of both Larry and Jon at Dogwise, as well as your commitment to providing book after excellent book on animal training and behavior.

I am deeply grateful to my students for their willingness to open yourselves to learning and your tireless efforts to apply your knowledge to their human and animal clients. Thank you for putting your trust in me, for showing up to learn, for asking hard questions and for bringing science into the hands-on aspects of our field. You all amaze and humble me every day and I am so grateful to be able to be a part of your journey.

And, finally, a huge heartfelt thank you to Brendan and Alex for your endless patience while I spent long hours working and for never doubting me. Words cannot express how amazing you are. I love you both so very, very much.

Foreword

by Irith Bloom

I first met Dr. Kristina Spaulding when we served together on the APDT Education Committee. I could tell right away how brilliant and insightful she was, and how lucky we were to have her on the team. Since those days, I have had the privilege and honor of working with Kristina in many different capacities. Every encounter with her is both a pleasure and a learning opportunity, and I am proud to call her my friend.

Kristina views behavior with an objective and critical eye. While she is willing to try methods that are only supported by informal or anecdotal experience, she also takes the time to delve deeper into how and why those methods work. Kristina is the epitome of what a scientist should be, and her approach to addressing behavior problems is built on a foundation of data and evidence.

One of Kristina's many amazing qualities is her enthusiasm for sharing her knowledge. I have been the beneficiary of her teaching skills countless times, both in formal and informal settings. As a scientist and Certified Applied Animal Behaviorist, Kristina has helped numerous clients struggling with problematic behavior in their dogs. She also has a knack for making scientific research both interesting and accessible – you could call that her superpower. I recommend Kristina's courses and presentations to everyone I meet, and I am thrilled she has a book I can recommend now as well.

The Stress Factor in Dogs is a distillation of knowledge Kristina has amassed over many years of working both in academia and with clients. In it, she lays out the relevant science on stress and behavior, both in general and as it specifically applies to dogs. She explains in clear terms why a lot of problematic dog behavior happens, and what to do to help dogs succeed in human homes.

Kristina has collated and analyzed the results of literally hundreds of research studies to get at the most crucial information for people working with dogs. While many of the concepts she discusses are complex, she makes everything understandable. She even goes out of her way to tell us when the science doesn't give a simple answer (or even any answer, in some cases)! A true educator, Kristina also takes the time to remind us that science is always developing and changing, so it's important to regularly re-evaluate everything we think we know.

The Stress Factor in Dogs is a thorough dive into the science of stress, but it goes well beyond that. It is also designed to give people the tools they need to help their dogs live happier, less stressful lives. It's a step-by-step explanation of how your dog got where he or she is today, and what you can do to make things better.

Change works best when we understand why we are making a change, so Kristina starts out by explaining stress in general terms. There's a lot more to stress than you may realize! Kristina talks about what stress is and how it affects the body. She then takes us on a journey through the variety of experiences that fall under the general umbrella of stress – including good stress, tolerable stress, and toxic stress – using down-to-earth examples. From how stress affects the body to how stress changes the brain, everything is laid out in plain language and backed by published research. In addition, Kristina reminds us that stress affects both learning and memory, which obviously has a variety of implications for the training we do with dogs.

Kristina also discusses the factors, such as genetics and developmental environment (to name just two), that lead some animals to respond differently to stress than others. How well animals respond to stress can be referred to as stress resiliency. Stress resiliency is a fairly new field of study, so there is not that much research on it. Kristina presents the current science on the topic and helps us make sense of it, all while reminding us to keep an open mind since there is still so much to learn about stress resiliency.

Best of all, Kristina's guidance goes well beyond helping us identify stressful situations (or even just figuring out our dog's level of stress resiliency). She lays out techniques and tips for reducing stress and increasing stress resiliency. From appropriate management of triggers, to increasing control and agency, to adding more effective enrichment, if there's a tool to help dogs live better lives, Kristina tells you about it. She also highlights research on stress in shelter, working, and performance dogs, and gives you a primer for how to read a scientific paper critically so you can continue your learning long after you finish this book.

Whether you are a professional helping clients with their dogs, or you share your life with dogs and want to understand them better, *The Stress Factor in Dogs* is for you. It is an invaluable resource that should be on everyone's bookshelf. I am blessed to have gotten this advance peek at it, and excited for everyone else to read it!

Irith Bloom, CPDT-KSA, CBCC-KA, CDBC, CSAT, KPA CTP, VSPDT, CBATI, FFCP (Trainer), VSDTA Faculty, DWA Faculty, sought-after presenter, and author of *Your Puppy and You: A Step-by-Step Guide to Raising a Freak'n Awesome Dog.*

Introduction

I will never forget the dog that started me on the journey to write this book. He was a tan and black fluffy mixed breed named Onyx, somewhere in the range of 60 lbs. Super cute. The client, Miguel, adopted him at around four months from a litter that was found abandoned along the side of the road. They were passed from one rescue to another and, as a result, Miguel's was probably the fourth or fifth home this young puppy had seen. Onyx had fear issues—with other dogs and people—from the very beginning. Miguel contacted several different dog professionals in an attempt to help Onyx. First, he was told to bring the terrified puppy to daycare to get him socialized. It was too much for Onyx and he spent most of the time hiding and trying to avoid the other dogs. Miguel quickly decided that method wasn't working, and moved on to another professional, who told him to bring Onyx to puppy classes in a big box store, which was also too overwhelming. After a string of trainers who were not able to help, Miguel eventually gave up and managed with Onyx on his own as best he could.

Over time, Onyx grew more anxious, aggressive and dangerous. Miguel met a woman named Stacy and they got married when Onyx was a couple of years old. Stacy had a miniature poodle that Onyx had attacked on multiple occasions, and they were concerned about the poodle's safety. Onyx had also shown aggression toward Miguel, the wife, visitors and dogs outside the household in a variety of contexts. Stacy wanted to get rid of Onyx, but Miguel loved him deeply and didn't want to give up on him. Miguel felt desperate. It was at this point that Miguel contacted me. Unfortunately, by that time,

Onyx had a history of several serious bites to both other dogs and people. There was little we could do to make sure that other animals and people could be safe around Onyx. Miguel made the heartbreaking decision to have Onyx euthanized.

This story impacted me so much because Miguel was incredibly dedicated to Onyx and had tried from a very early age to find help. There are *many* reasons that this story ended in heartbreak, but I believe that one likely major contributing factor was that Onyx experienced chronic stress throughout his development. When Miguel adopted Onyx, he was already at very high risk of behavior issues. Nevertheless, this information was never communicated to Miguel despite all the contact he had with rescue volunteers, dog trainers, veterinarians and staff. When we met and I explained to him how deeply and dramatically stress can impact behavior and welfare, it was all new to him.

I can't help but wonder if things would have been different if there had been an awareness from the beginning that Onyx was at high risk for behavior issues. Perhaps with a greater recognition of the impacts of stress on behavior, and an understanding of how to reduce the impacts of stress, things would have turned out differently for Onyx. Miguel could have been taught how to avoid putting Onyx in overwhelming situations and steps could have been taken to try to increase Onyx's stress coping skills. Unfortunately, it is too late to change the outcome for Onyx. We'll never know if appropriate and skilled early intervention would have changed the outcome for him. However, there are thousands and thousands of other dogs that still need our help. We can never reduce the risk to zero, but there are many things we can do to give stressed dogs and their people the best chance they can have at a good life. My hope in writing this book is that I will give you, dear reader, the tools you need to do just that. I hope this book will bring hope to dogs that have been struggling with stress—and to the people that love and care for them.

Stress impacts behavior

The premise of this book is that stress impacts behavior. While some stress can be beneficial, stress often results in problematic behavior for dog owners. By gaining a thorough understanding of stress in dogs, you will be better able to prevent and deal with issues that may impact the welfare and behavior of your dog, including:

- Aggression
- Excessive barking
- Fear and anxiety
- High arousal and reactivity

A focus on welfare and well-being

This book is about stress, but ultimately the goal is to help you provide your dog with a better life. Stress is closely related to an animal's quality of life. There are two terms that come up frequently when talking about quality of life and I'd like to define them here because I will be discussing them later in the book. **Welfare** usually refers to making sure an animal's basic needs are met in order to reduce suffering. This includes things like access to adequate food, water, and shelter. The concept of **well-being** has become more prominent recently. It goes beyond the concept of welfare by including the experience of positive emotions in animals. You can think of welfare as eliminating negative emotions and experiences and well-being as increasing resilience, positive emotions and experiences. If we really want to maximize quality of life for animals, then we want to focus on both welfare and well-being.

How this book is organized

The book starts with an explanation of what stress is and, very generally, how it impacts the dog. Chapter 1 sets the backdrop for the rest of the book. In Chapter 2, I will discuss the stress response itself and how it works. I try to lay out the key points—the things you need to know to truly understand stress—without getting overly technical. The information in this chapter will help you understand the rest of the book. Once you understand how the stress response affects the body, it will really open your eyes to how stress has such a major effect on behavior.

From there, we move onto Chapter 3, which covers the impacts of stress throughout life. Stress does not impact dogs equally throughout development. Dogs are more vulnerable during some stages of life than others. Chapter 3 explores those stages and explains the unique influences of stress at each of those periods. Understanding how stress can impact dogs across their lifetime helps us protect them when they are at their most vulnerable.

Stress also has a number of impacts on learning and memory. This has obvious implications for training dogs! Chapter 4 goes into detail about the effect of stress on learning and memory. We are primarily interested in two types of learning—learning behaviors and learning what is safe and not safe. Stress impacts both types of learning. It has very important impacts on fear learning, as well as the recovery from fear and can influence the types of behavior a dog is likely to exhibit. It is hard to avoid a discussion of learning and stress without talking about trauma, and Chapter 4 talks about that as well.

In Chapter 5, I turn the corner a bit, and start to discuss the idea of resilience. **Resilience** has to do with how well a dog copes with stress. Dogs that are better at coping with stress will enjoy a better quality of life and be less likely to develop behavior issues. Therefore, we really want to have resilient dogs! In order to build resilience, we first need to understand how it develops. Chapter 5 is focused on why some dogs are more resilient than others.

Understanding how resiliency develops is key to understanding how to promote it. And that's what Chapter 6 is all about! This chapter talks about how to reduce stress and increase stress resilience in dogs, which ultimately will help decrease behavior issues and improve the quality of life for dogs and their families.

Chapter 7 addresses stress in specific populations (like shelter, working and performance dogs) and the impact of training methods on stress. We do not have as much research on these topics as we do on stress and resilience in general. The good news is that the information we do have is specific to dogs and is very applicable to the real world. This chapter is definitely worth a read! The information on training methods will be useful to everyone.

Chapter 8 offers concluding thoughts that tie together the ideas from the entire book. But don't stop there! Don't miss the Appendix on the scientific method and understanding and interpreting research. The study of dog behavior is exploding right now and shows no signs of slowing down. New studies are coming out every day. This is incredible news for those of us that love dogs.

Do yourself a favor and read the Appendix, even if you are hesitant! It will help you be a better consumer of scientific research and allow you to read and effectively interpret and apply new research that comes out about dogs. That will make you a better trainer and caretaker of dogs.

A note on research, other species and style

In this book, I give you the information we have based on the current research, and I share some of my own thoughts as well. My dearest hope is that you will also take this information and use it to generate your own ideas about how to apply this information to improve the lives of dogs (or whatever species you work with)! You might want to get a little notebook and keep it at your side while you read—that way you can jot down any ideas you have about addressing or preventing stress in your or your clients' dogs. Then you can go back later, pick the ideas that are most promising and start to implement them! Imagine what a difference it could make if every person who reads this book comes up with and shares one new idea for helping dogs.

Before moving on, I want to mention that the focus of this book is on dogs because that is the species I work with and am most knowledgeable about. However, the principles of stress apply to other animals as well. The stress response and its effects on the body and behavior appear to be remarkably consistent across mammals. So, if you work with other mammal species, this material should be highly applicable to those species as well. Much of the research is also consistent in birds, reptiles and amphibians as well, but I am not very familiar with the research on those species, and I would be more cautious about broadly applying what you read here to animals that are not mammals.

Because some of the research is done on rodents and because it applies so widely to so many species, I often use the word "animal" instead of "dog." That is because I want to make it clear that the information is not true just for dogs. However, when research has been done specifically on dogs, I will point that out and use dog instead of animal. Also, because this book is dog focused, I tend to use dog when I am speaking in general terms and not referring to specific research. However, you could easily substitute another mammal species for dog, like cat, or horse.

Throughout the book, I try to alternate gender when speaking of both dogs and people. Therefore, you will sometimes see me use "he" or "she" and sometimes "her" or "him." Key words are bolded and defined on first use. Names of clients and dogs, and any potentially identifying details, have been changed to maintain privacy.

You may find this book stressful

Reading about stress is stressful. There are parts of this book that were difficult to write because there is so much emphasis on suffering. I know that it's painful and I also believe that the only way through that pain is, well, through it. If we square our shoulders and step into that world with an open heart and open mind, we will learn how incredibly damaging stress can be. That understanding is what gives us the empathy and motivation to do something about it. When we come through to the other side of the tough stuff, the solutions are there waiting for us.

On that note, it's time to get started. Find a cozy place, get comfy and get reading!

Chapter 1
What is Stress?

We are all familiar with feelings of stress. We might experience stress when we are running late to an important meeting, ending a relationship, or worrying about money. We identify stress in our dogs as well; for example, when they visit the veterinarian, or during a thunderstorm. But what is stress, really? And how exactly does it influence behavior?

Definition and function of stress

Stress is a reaction to change. More specifically, stress is the body's response to a trigger which disrupts—or potentially disrupts—the status quo. The trigger is known as a **stressor**. The stressor can be something physical, such as getting sick, that directly challenges a dog's **physiological** systems. If a dog is sick, for example, it may throw the dog's normal body systems out of whack. The stressor can also be psychosocial, which means it relates to the social environment and social interactions. An example of a psychosocial stressor is a new dog entering the home, altering the resident dog's social environment and, therefore, altering the dog's status quo. Being in a new home is also a psychosocial stressor for the new dog.

Stressors can also be actual or perceived. Imagine a dog named Shadow who is afraid of strangers and barks when they come to visit. The stranger is not *actually* threatening Shadow's physical safety. However, if Shadow associates the stranger with threat or *believes* the stranger might attack him, then that still causes stress. Of course, we can't know what's really going on inside Shadow's head, but if he is displaying defensive behavior, I think it's safe to say that he perceives a threat.

Here are several more examples of stressors from the human perspective: caring for a loved one with a terminal illness, taking an exam, breaking a bone, the holidays. What about from the dog's perspective? Going to a dog show, fireworks, breaking a bone, the holidays.

In all these examples there is some actual or perceived trigger that is threatening (or perceived to threaten) the animal's status quo. This triggers a **stress response** which is a very specific physiological reaction involving the release of chemicals that help regulate the body's physiological system (more on this later).

Evolution and stress

Stress itself is not "bad." In fact, in many cases stress—and the stress response—is beneficial and adaptive. Stress helps the body adjust to and cope with change. It helps animals to survive in moments of immediate threat. That is, in fact, the adaptive function of stress. For dogs, stress helped them survive over thousands of years by being able to effectively react to and cope with threats.

Peter Gluckman and his colleagues were one of the first to suggest that the reason stress-induced changes occur is to prepare an animal for living a life of struggle (Gluckman et al., 2007). If mom is highly stressed during pregnancy, then it is likely the offspring will be stressed as well. If a dog is living in a high-risk environment, then the stress response should be primed to respond to threats. If a dog can keep alive long enough to breed and pass on its genes to the next generation, this is a victory from an evolutionary perspective. However, problems can arise when a dog learns to cope with a high-stress environment early in life, but ends up living in a safe environment (like a pet home).

Acute vs. chronic stress

Stress can be acute or chronic. **Acute stress** occurs when the stressor is relatively short-lived—generally less than a few weeks—though there is no hard and fast time frame. Acute stress could be momentary. For example, slamming on your brakes because the car in front of you stopped quickly, or your dog hearing a sudden and startling loud noise. Examples of slightly longer acute stressors include rushing to meet a deadline at work or kenneling a dog for several days. Dogs usually cope fairly well with acute stress. The physiological response does its job—protecting the animal from a potential threat—and then the body carries on as usual. However, in some cases, a single event is severe enough—for example a serious car accident or being attacked by another dog—to have lasting effects.

Chronic stress occurs when an animal experiences repeated stressors in relatively close succession. In general, stress is considered chronic if it lasts for weeks or longer, with each day involving an extended period of stress (Protopopova, 2016; McEwen, 2017). In contrast to acute stress, chronic stress has several serious negative impacts on both emotional and physical health—we will cover this in detail in Chapters 3 and 4.

Good, tolerable and toxic stress

Stress can also be subdivided based on whether it's beneficial, neutral, or harmful. The late Bruce McEwen at Rockefeller University was one of the leading researchers on the topic of stress. He divided stress into three categories: good stress, tolerable stress and toxic stress (McEwen, 2017).

Good stress

With good stress, an individual experiences a healthy challenge that can be a rewarding experience. It involves "rising to a challenge, taking a risk and feeling rewarded by an often positive outcome." (McEwan, 2017, p. 2). Good stress is often referred to as **eustress**. You can think of eustress as a form of stress that increases the animal's ability to interact effectively with their environment. This could be something like teaching a dog a new skill. Imagine a dog that is learning agility. Foxy starts off unsure of the tunnel, but the trainer does an excellent job of breaking the skill into manageable pieces, letting Foxy go at her own pace and reinforcing her progress. Eventually, the tunnel becomes Foxy's favorite obstacle! In this case, the situation was initially challenging, but it was never actually distressing, and Foxy ended up better off in the long run.

Compared to bad stress, eustress has gotten very little attention. Just to give you an idea, if you did a search in 2020 for "distress" in Google Scholar, you get over 3.5 million results. Eustress has just over 25,000! This follows a general trend in psychology where the tendency is to focus on the mental illness aspects of psychology, rather than wellness. Luckily (in my opinion), this has been changing in recent years. The most important point is that stress is not automatically "bad"—it can have positive effects as well.

Tolerable stress

When an individual experiences tolerable stress, he or she has a negative experience, but can cope with that experience, often with help from social support. Both good stress and tolerable stress can result in growth when the individual is resilient enough to cope with and adapt to the stressful experience. In many cases the individual emerges from the experience stronger than before. Some distress falls into the category of tolerable stress—the experience itself is unpleasant and uncomfortable—but it does not have major long-term effects.

An example of tolerable stress could be taking a shy dog named Teddy for a walk. For the first couple of walks, Teddy is very anxious, but eventually he gets more comfortable and comes to loves walks. This experience then generalizes to walks in other places and Teddy becomes more confident overall. In this case, the experience was initially distressing, but it ended up being beneficial in the long run. (Note that it doesn't always happen like this! In some cases, the dog may become more and more fearful. More on this later—keep reading!)

Toxic stress

Toxic stress is a different beast entirely. When a dog experiences toxic stress, bad things happen, and the dog is unable to effectively cope. This could be because they have limited access to coping behaviors. For example, a dog who is kept in a crate or outdoor kennel and socially isolated does not have access to natural behaviors that may help alleviate the negative impacts of stress. Another reason a dog may not be able to cope is because her brain cannot respond appropriately to stress for one reason or another. You will learn later in the book how early exposure to stress can dramatically impair an animal's ability to cope with stress later in life.

In the case of toxic stress, the animal also experiences distress, but of much greater intensity. The degree of stress exceeds the animal's ability to cope. This might be a dog that goes through a move and develops separation anxiety or a dog that completely panics over a nail trim. Usually acute stress is not toxic. However, there are exceptions to this. For example, acute stress could be toxic if it is extreme (i.e., trauma), or if a dog is particularly vulnerable to the impacts of stress for some reason. Chronic stress is considered toxic stress. It is safe to assume that when I say chronic stress, that is a form of toxic stress. The vast majority of the research on stress has also been done on chronic stress, so you'll see me mentioning chronic stress in the following chapters more often than toxic stress.

There is a long list of effects from toxic stress. The impacts of toxic and chronic stress are covered in detail in chapters three and four, but the following is a brief summary.

Impacts of toxic stress

Chronic stress has a wide range of impacts and has been much more widely studied. It's associated with **stress-related psychiatric disorders** such as post-traumatic stress disorder (PTSD) and depression in people and PTSD- and depression-like behaviors in animals (Sandi and Haller, 2015; Schöner et al., 2017; and Cruz-Pereira et al., 2020). Chronic stress also increases the likelihood of aggression and decreases social interaction (Beerda et al., 1999; van der Kooij et al., 2014). It can have negative impacts on memory and cognition, and it decreases cardiovascular, metabolic and immune function (Juster et al., 2010; McEwen, 2017). For example, one study found that people under stress showed weaker and/or shorter-lived immune responses to vaccines (Glaser and Kiecolt-Glaser, 2005). Stressed individuals also heal more slowly from wounds (Kiecolt-Glaser et al., 1995; Padgett et al., 1998). Chronic stress can even shorten the lifespan and increase the risk of death (Seeman et al., 2001)!

Chronic stress is bad. So clearly the answer is to make sure that everything in the dog's world is always sunshine and rainbows, right? It is easy to think that, but preventing all stress isn't the answer either! We obviously want to do our best to avoid traumatic experiences, as well as to minimize or prevent chronic distress, but remember that some stress is beneficial.

Most of the research into toxic stress has focused on that which is chronic. However acute stress can have negative impacts as well. For example, in certain contexts acute stress can increase aggression as well as **antisocial behavior** in rodents (Sandi and Haller, 2015). Sandi and Haller define antisocial behavior as behaviors that "...break behavioural 'rules' that have evolved to limit dangerous forms of aggression. They include excessive levels of...[aggression] and deficient social communication." And this is something we want to avoid!

There is something else going on here that I want to make sure I point out. Maybe you've realized it already—the stressor itself is not the most important element in determining whether stress is good, tolerable or toxic. *It's the individual's ability to cope with that stressor that matters the most. In other words, the most important factor is how resilient the dog is.*

Let's go back to the example of Teddy going for a walk. Initially, Teddy was afraid, but he eventually grew to love not only that park, but others as well. Contrast this with Ella who goes for a walk and is so scared that she's not able to acclimate. Her owner, not knowing any better, continues to bring her on walks. Walks become a source of chronic stress for Ella. Her behavior and emotional health begin to deteriorate. In this case, Teddy was able to cope with the stressor of walks, so it was tolerable stress for him. Ella was *not* able to cope with that same stress, so it was toxic stress for her. What's important here is that we can't change the fact that there is a stressor, but we often *can* change the dog's reaction to that stressor, at least to a degree. The concept of resilience will be discussed in detail in Chapters 5 and 6.

Now that you have a good understanding of what stress is, we'll discuss how stress affects the body in the next chapter.

Chapter 2
The Physiology of Stress

As dog lovers, it's important that we understand the physiology of stress. A more concrete understanding of how stress works in dogs and affects their bodies (and behavior) will help us address stress more effectively. Physiological stress responses follow a predictable pattern in healthy dogs. It is important to understand this pattern because it will come into play later when we talk about the impacts of stress on the brain and behavior.

All about stress hormones

When a dog experiences a stressor, the body prepares itself for action. The first thing that responds is the sympathetic nervous system. The sympathetic nervous system signals the release of **epinephrine** and **norepinephrine** (formerly called adrenaline and noradrenaline).

Shortly after the sympathetic nervous system kicks in, the **hypothalamic-pituitary-adrenal** (HPA) axis becomes activated. It is important to know this term as it comes up very frequently in stress research. However, it is probably easier to remember it as the **HPA-axis**. The hypothalamus begins a cascade of events that eventually triggers the release of stress hormones (**glucocorticoids**) from the adrenal glands.

In humans and dogs, the primary stress hormone is **cortisol**. In rodents, it is **corticosterone**. I will simply refer to them as **stress hormones**. There is relatively little research on stress done directly on dogs, but there is a very large body of research from rodents. Luckily for us, the effects of stress hormones are extremely similar across mammals, despite having slightly different types of stress hormones (Selye, 1950). The research that has been done on dogs supports the idea that their behavioral and physiological responses to stress are similar to the responses of other mammals, including rodents (Beerda et al., 1998, 1999, 2000).

Stress hormones and the fight-or-flight response

The activation of the sympathetic nervous systems and the HPA axis prepares the body to mobilize its energy resources—this is known as the fight-or-flight response. This activation has several immediate effects (Lupien et al., 2009):

- Heart and breathing rate, blood pressure, and access to energy all increase.
- Attention and memory of important details increase.
- Pain perception decreases.
- The brain switches to more habitual responses that bypass careful thought (Schwabe et al., 2007; Schwabe and Wolf, 2009).

All these actions prepare the animal to fight or flee (or in some cases, freeze). This makes sense from a survival standpoint. If your life is in danger, it pays to be more aware of your surroundings. You don't want to waste time fretting over a stubbed toe or agonizing over whether to run to the left or the right. It also pays to remember that experience. If you do survive, remembering the key details of *how* you survived may help protect you in the future. The body focuses all its resources on systems that are needed in the moment to aid survival. That means it diverts resources *away from* any systems that are not immediately needed for survival. Those include the reproductive, growth and digestive systems. In this way, the stress response affects multiple systems in the body.

Higher levels of stress hormones may be linked to passive coping in the form of freezing. Scientists are still working out the details behind these behaviors, but there is evidence that stress hormones are involved in the freezing response. One thing we know is that increased levels of stress hormones are associated with increased freezing and avoidance and decreased approach (Koolhaas et al., 1999). It takes some time for stress hormones to reach *peak* levels after being exposed to a stressor. However, neurological research suggests that the specific mechanisms involved in the freezing response are activated at low stress hormone levels, allowing animals to freeze almost immediately, rather than several minutes after the fact (Koolhaas et al., 1999).

Different perspectives, same physiological responses
My dogs love chasing chipmunks. When they go outside and encounter a chipmunk, their bodies go rigid, their tails go straight up and then they take off after the chipmunk. This is often accompanied by a lot of panting and vocalizing—clear signs of excitement. The chipmunks, in the meantime, run as fast as they can for safety. One animal is having fun and one animal is running for its life, but both animals are having a similar physiological stress response.

Equilibrium: homeostasis and allostasis

In healthy animals, a **negative feedback loop** ends the stress response once the stressor has diminished. When the stress hormones reach a certain level, the body signals the shutdown of stress hormone production. Think of the thermostat in your house. Let's say you set it to 70 degrees. When it's above 70 degrees, the thermostat sends a signal to the furnace and the furnace turns off. This is an example of a negative feedback loop. Then, when the temperature goes under 70 degrees another signal gets sent, and the furnace turns on. This keeps the temperature of your house at or very close to 70 degrees. The body does the same thing with stress hormone levels. Basically, there is a built-in safety valve to prevent overproduction of stress hormones.

This state of equilibrium is known as **homeostasis** and it's often used to explain how animals maintain a stable physiological state. The body strives to maintain homeostasis—or stability—around ideal set points for a variety of different measures. Examples of these measures include glucose levels, heart rate, body temperature and, of course, stress hormone levels. When their bodies stray too far from the ideal level, signals are sent, and the system corrects itself. The traditional medical model considers animals who successfully maintain homeostasis as healthy.

Until recently, this is how the stress system—and physiology in general—was explained. However, lately that view of physiology has been challenged. A new term, called **allostasis**, has been coined to label this new viewpoint. Allostasis is different from homeostasis in that the setpoint is not set in stone—it changes based on current conditions (Sterling and Eyer, 1988; McEwen and Mirsky, 2018). Allostasis describes the process through which animals adjust their internal state and physiology to adjust to the changing environment.

According to this theory, health is the ability to *respond and adapt to changes* in your environment (Sterling, 2004). The allostasis theory proposes that the body may be a more dynamic system, so after experiencing change, the body can adjust to arrive at a different set point. The allostasis viewpoint is more integrated than the classic homeostasis perspective. It looks at the body as an entire, interconnected system that communicates with itself (Schulkin, 2003; Juster et al., 2010). From this perspective, health and aging well can be considered indicators of an individual's ability to successfully adapt to life's changes.

Physiological responses to chronic stress

When an animal experiences a stressor, it needs to adjust to a new normal—or a new allostatic set point. Again, stress hormone levels are regulated through a negative feedback loop. When stress hormone levels become too high, a signal is sent that shuts down their production.

However, the process of repeated adjustments is taxing and exacts a toll on the body. The accumulated cost of these repeated adjustments is known as **allostatic load** (McEwen and Stellar, 1993). When the stress response systems are chronically overworked due to chronic stress, the allostatic load can become overwhelming. Eventually, the negative feedback loop stops working and when this happens the systems begin to collapse (Sánchez et al., 2001; Lupien et al., 2009; Burke et al., 2017). This creates a state known as **allostatic overload** and makes the animal vulnerable to a number of stress-related disorders (Korte et al., 2005; Juster et al., 2010).

When allostatic overload occurs, the HPA axis becomes dysregulated. This results in several dramatic and alarming impacts on behavior, health and cognition. Prominent stress researcher Bruce McEwen (2017) explains this as follows. A healthy brain is flexible and resilient. It can easily adapt to a changing environment. However, an unhealthy brain (one damaged by toxic stress) is less flexible. Therefore, the unhealthy brain is less able to adapt. In this case, the individual may need medication or behavior modification in order to cope with the environment.

Why does this happen? Being exposed to stress—particularly during key developmental stages—causes a series of changes to the brain and body that are very harmful. Among other things, chronic stress changes the size of certain brain areas. It also changes how neurons and connections between neurons in the brain are structured. These changes make it difficult for the brain to adapt to additional stressors. The constant, high levels of stress hormones start to damage the body (McEwen, 2017). This causes other systems in the body to change as well, which leads to further dysregulation (Juster et al., 2010). Everything is connected; nothing in the body acts in isolation.

If the stress response system goes haywire, this causes other systems to overcompensate. Then those systems get dysregulated as well. It reminds me of many years ago when I injured my ankle. The doctor told me that by limping to take weight off my left ankle, I would create problems in other parts of my body. Since I was not moving normally due to the injured ankle, other parts of my body were compensating for that unusual movement and muscle use. Because that is not how those muscles were designed to work, it would eventually create other problems. I'm sure you can imagine that if an animal is experiencing physiological chaos, that will impact many other things, including their behavior. More on the behavior aspect later!

The secondary systems that get dysregulated include the metabolic, cardiovascular and immune systems. With so many systems dysregulated, body systems in general begin to collapse (Juster et al., 2010). When this happens, the animal is experiencing allostatic overload. Allostatic overload is no joke. It results in death and disease (no, I am not exaggerating). Possible results of allostatic overload include depression, PTSD, diabetes, heart disease and a shortened life span, among others (Seeman et al., 1997; Seeman et al., 2001; Juster et al., 2010).

There has been very little research on this topic in dogs, but at least one study has found a correlation between anxiety, health and lifespan in dogs. Researcher Nancy Dreschel (2010) found that dogs with fear and separation anxiety had more frequent and more severe skin issues. In the same study, fear of strangers was associated with decreased lifespan. (See the Appendix for important guidance on interpreting correlations in research.)

There is also ample evidence from the rodent literature that indicates that stress leads to multiple issues down the road. You can also see this in the real world. Many of us have probably encountered dogs with a history of stressful life experiences. Many of these dogs also suffer from a long list of health and behavior issues. This is especially true for those of us who have worked in shelter or rescue environments or work with dogs with behavior issues. In many cases, chronic stress likely contributes to the development of those issues.

One active area of research right now is trying to find ways to concretely measure, or **operationalize**, these changes. A number of labs are looking into how certain measures of stress and allostatic load translate into actual physical health. Seeman and colleagues (1997) found that higher allostatic load was associated with decreased cognitive and physical performance. Over three years, people with higher allostatic load had greater declines in cognitive and physical functioning compared to those with lower allostatic load. That was true even after accounting for current health and socioeconomic status (two other big predictors of health). Interestingly, none of the individual markers on its own was a reliable predictor of functioning—only when the markers were *combined* did they find an association. That is, single measures, such as epinephrine (adrenaline) or blood pressure, were not associated with decreased functioning, but if you combined ten different measures, then a pattern would emerge.

People with higher allostatic load also had an increased risk of mortality from *any* cause after seven years (which is when they followed up with participants from the original study) (Seeman et al., 2001). The good news is that if you decrease allostatic load, the risk of dying also decreases—and this is true even in older individuals (Karlamangla et al., 2006). This is good news for our dogs (and people!) because it means that even if you have an animal that is highly stressed and has been for a long time, reducing their level of stress can still have very important, measurable impacts.

As with many aspects of physiology, the stress hormones are not involved only in the stress response. They are also play an important role in the brain. As a result, toxic stress can alter the structure and function of the brain.

How stress impacts brain structure and function

The impact of toxic stress varies in different areas of the brain, but the hippocampus, amygdala and prefrontal cortex seem to be particularly impacted by stress. These three brain areas also play an important role in the regulation of emotion, the evaluation of threat and social behavior.

The hippocampus plays a critical role in the regulation of the HPA axis, context learning and the decrease of learned fear. Chronic stress causes damage to the hippocampus (Conrad, 2008; Lupien et al., 2009). For example, stress leads to a reduction of dendritic branching in the hippocampus (Fenoglio et al., 2006). Dendritic branching is important for communication between neurons. The more dendritic branching, the more efficient the brain. Reduced dendritic branching in the hippocampus indicates that it's functioning below normal levels.

Damage to the hippocampus also impairs context learning (Maren, 2011). This is very important! Context learning means that a dog learns to associate a particular context, such as a vet clinic, with something scary. This helps limit the fear to that context. The hippocampus sends information about a particular context to other brain areas. This information helps those brain areas determine those other contexts which have *not* been associated with something scary or unpleasant. As a result, the animal doesn't display fear in those contexts. When the hippocampus is damaged, animals are no longer able to contextualize fear. Therefore, the fear becomes generalized to a variety of contexts, even if the animal has never had an unpleasant experience in those contexts. This is what can lead to a dog displaying global fear regardless of where they are—they are no longer able to distinguish between safe and unsafe situations, so everything becomes frightening (Maren, 2011; McMillan, 2020).

Both the hippocampus and the prefrontal cortex are involved in the extinction of fear. If they are damaged, it will be harder to decrease fear in that animal. It's worth noting that this failure of extinction is thought to be one of the main deficits behind the persistence of PTSD symptoms (Van Elzakker et al., 2014). Indeed, there is evidence that people with PTSD have smaller hippocampal volume than the rest of the population (Woon et al., 2010).

The hippocampus also plays an important role in various types of memory. It is believed that many of the cognitive impairments associated with chronic stress are a result of damage to the hippocampus (Fenster, 2018).

The **amygdala** is another brain area that tends to be impacted by stress. The amygdala is heavily involved in fear and anxiety. Stress seems to *enhance* amygdala activity (Lupien et al., 2009; Fenster, 2018), making the animal more susceptible to fear and anxiety. Combine increased amygdala activity with a damaged hippocampus and a more active stress response system and you have an animal that is primed to develop behavior issues.

Finally, stress impairs the function of the prefrontal cortex. Outside of scientific circles, the amygdala seems to get a lot more attention than the prefrontal cortex, but the prefrontal cortex plays a critically important role in fear and fear-related symptoms. One of the primary jobs of the prefrontal cortex is to regulate other brain areas. The prefrontal cortex helps regulate emotion, including fear and aggression (Siever, 2008). If the prefrontal cortex is damaged, it is less able to hold back strong emotions, leading to increased emotionality and impulsivity.

So, here is the big picture. Stress and trauma appear to damage the hippocampus and the prefrontal cortex, while enhancing activity in the amygdala. Both the hippocampus and prefrontal cortex play an important role in extinction, so if they are damaged, it will be harder for the animal to experience a decrease in fear through extinction. Furthermore, the hippocampus helps the animal determine whether or not a particular situation is safe. If it is damaged, the animal can lose the ability to distinguish between safe and unsafe situations and starts reacting as if *all* situations are unsafe. This can lead to generalized fear and anxiety. On top of that, the amygdala is over-active so it's responding more strongly to more triggers, which means a wide variety of stimuli are setting off a fear and anxiety response. Finally, the prefrontal cortex is not as able to do its job of tamping down all of that emotionality because it's not working as well either. Can you see why stress can have such a profound and difficult to reverse impact on fear and anxiety?

Stress hormones are also important for brain development and maturation. If the developing animal gets lower *or* higher than normal levels of stress hormones during development, it can have major impacts on development and behavior. (Lupien et al., 2009)

Stress hormones and development

Stress hormones have a number of important developmental roles. These roles include promoting cell survival and the development, structure and connections of neurons. In addition, the fetal brain is very flexible and its development changes based on environmental signals. So, stress during development can *literally* change how the brain is wired (Meyer, 1983; Seckl, 2008). Organs are most vulnerable during periods of development. The brain has a particularly long period of development—from gestation to adolescence—so it is especially sensitive to the impacts of stress. In humans and rodents, the brain is still undergoing dramatic development during puberty (Lupien et al., 2009; Brenhouse and Andersen, 2011). Unfortunately, we do not have this data in dogs, but it is likely they follow a similar pattern.

When the pregnant mother is stressed, her stress hormones pass through the placenta and cause increased HPA activity in the fetus (Seckl, 2008). This increased HPA activity can occur well past the prenatal period, even lasting into adulthood (Koehl et al., 1999). This can result in higher baseline levels of stress hormones and/or increase the release of stress hormones in response to stress (Sandi and Haller, 2015). Juvenile stress also causes changes to the brain. Rat pups that experience unnaturally long separations from their mothers (usually three hours or more each day) show increased levels of stress hormones (Levine & Wiener, 1988; Schulkin et al., 1998; Lupien et al., 2009). Maternal separation also causes changes to the brain—including the prefrontal cortex, amygdala and hippocampus.

The impacts of stress on the brain really highlight the importance of limiting toxic stress during development as well as minimizing stress when addressing of behavior issues. It is going to be very difficult to decrease fear and anxiety (which drive many behavior issues) when the dog's brain is marinating in a pool of stress hormones!

Now that you have a broad understanding of the negative impacts of toxic stress, let's discuss how stress impacts dogs throughout their lifetimes in more detail.

Chapter 3
Toxic Stress and Its Impacts on Behavior

This chapter will cover the impacts of toxic stress throughout a dog's lifetime. Stress impacts animals differently at different ages. Understanding when dogs are most vulnerable can help us intervene early on to minimize the impacts of toxic stress. Development (prenatal through adolescence) is a particularly vulnerable period. Chronic stress during this time can have a profound impact on behavior. Once animals move from adolescence into adulthood, they are less vulnerable. This doesn't mean there are no longer negative impacts of stress, but adults tend to be more resilient in general than younger animals (Lupien et al., 2009). Once animals become seniors, however, they become vulnerable to stress yet again.

Most of the research done on stress has been done on rodents. Numerous studies have been done on other species as well, including dogs, but by far the greatest number have been conducted on rats and mice. For that reason, many of the studies referenced below are studies on rodents. Whenever possible, I included research that has been done on dogs. Remember, research on stress in mammals other than rodents has been remarkably consistent, suggesting that the impacts of stress on the brain and behavior are consistent across mammals (including humans). Therefore, I feel confident using research conducted on all mammal species to draw conclusions about dog behavior. I believe this research can provide the proper roadmap to better understand stress in dogs.

Prenatal stress

Here is a common scenario. A pregnant mom comes into the shelter. She is malnourished and is suffering from parasites. She is terrified of the shelter workers and spends most of her time hiding in the back of the kennel. The shelter gives her the food, shelter and health care she needs, and a few days later her puppies are born. In the best case, Mom and puppies will be placed into foster care. They receive excellent care, and the foster family makes socialization a priority. The puppies are adopted quickly, into carefully selected homes. Since birth, the puppies have had a pretty good start to life—how much does it matter that mom was stressed during pregnancy? Unfortunately, it can matter a lot even when the shelter and the family did everything right.

Exposure to prenatal stress can have dramatic and long-lasting effects on behavior. Prenatal stress can occur as a result of the mother being under psychosocial or physical stress. The mom mentioned above was under both types of stress.

Prenatal stress impacts on learning and cognition

Prenatal stress has several negative impacts on learning and cognition. Much of this research is highly specific and the details are too technical to cover in this book. In addition, cognition and memory tests conducted in a lab are usually very specific. For this reason, it can be difficult to imagine exactly how they impact behavior in the real world. However, it is likely that prenatal stress interferes with a dog's ability to learn new skills to some degree. Indeed, prenatal stress has been linked to a variety of impairments in learning, memory and attention (Benoit et al., 2015; Nazeri et al., 2015, Lemaire et al., 2000; Machado et al., 2015). Research in monkeys and rats suggests that chronic prenatal stress may reduce attention span and increase distractibility (Schneider and Coe, 1993; Wilson et al., 2012). Prenatal stress also impacts fear learning and extinction—this will be covered in more detail in Chapter 4.

Prenatal stress impacts on social behavior

Animals that are stressed prenatally may also show reduced social behavior later in life (Sandi & Haller, 2015; de Souza et al., 2013; Takahashi, 1992). In one study, pregnant rats were subjected to a variety of stressors for one week during pregnancy (Lee et al., 2007). The adult male offspring of the stressed moms spent *76%* less time interacting with another rat than the offspring of the non-stressed moms. When they did interact, they were less likely to make physical contact than non-stressed offspring. A similar response was seen in adolescent males—they spent 50% less time interacting. These patterns remained even in offspring that were fostered with moms that had not been stressed. This suggests that the changes happened *in utero* and were not just due to a change in mom's behavior. Another study found very similar results—males rats showed impaired social behavior when mom was stressed while pregnant. Again, this was true whether they were raised by their biological mother, or by a foster mother that was not stressed during pregnancy (de Souza et al., 2013). Research in prenatally stressed rhesus monkeys has also shown increased behavioral responsiveness to stress and abnormalities in social behavior (Clarke and Schneider, 1993).

Several studies suggest that prenatal stress reduces aggression later in life (Kinsley and Svare, 1986; Patin et al., 2005; Ogrizek et al., 2018). This may be due to an increase in fear and avoidance behavior, rather than a sign of good adjustment. It is also worth noting that research studies often distinguish between aggression, which is more proactive, and defensive behavior. A decrease in aggression in a lab study does not necessarily indicate a decrease in defensive behavior. Much of what we label as aggression in dogs is driven by fear (Dinwoodie et al., 2021; Mikkola et al., 2021). Therefore, research that indicates a reduction of aggression in lab rats does not *necessarily* indicate that pet dogs will be less likely to show growling, snapping or biting if they are fearful or anxious.

Prenatal stress impacts on anxiety-and depression-like behaviors

Anxiety and depression are characterized by particular emotional states and subjective experiences. We cannot know with certainty whether non-human animals, including dogs, experience anxiety and depression in the same way that humans do. However, it is widely accepted that animals can and do display behaviors that are consistent with the experience of anxiety and depression in humans (Weinstock, 2008). These behaviors are called **anxiety- and depression-like behaviors**.

There are many studies linking prenatal stress with increases in anxiety- and depression-like behaviors. This is true for humans as well as rodents (Secoli and Teixeira, 1998; Van den Bergh et al., 2008; Weinstock, 2008). There is some indication that females are more likely to show depression-like behaviors than males as a result of prenatal stress (Alonso et al., 1991; Keshet and Weinstock, 1995). The depression-like behaviors can show up in juveniles, adolescents and adults (Alonso et al., 2000; Guan et al., 2013; Rayen et al., 2011).

What does this behavior look like? Examples of anxiety-like behaviors include increased startle and reduced exploration. Two common tests of anxiety in rodents are the open field test and the elevated plus maze. In the open field test, animals are placed in a rectangular arena with walls on each side. Researchers record how much time animals spend in the corners as opposed to the central area. More time spent near the corners is believed to indicate higher level of anxiety because the animals are seeking a place of refuge. The elevated plus maze has four arms and is elevated above the ground. The arms intersect each other to make a plus sign. Two of the arms have high walls. Two of the arms have no walls at all, leaving the animal exposed. Animals that spend more time on the open arms are considered less anxious.

One of the early studies on prenatal stress and its impacts on anxiety was conducted by Vallée et al (1997). It provides a nice illustration of how these tests are used. Pregnant female rodents were stressed for 45 minutes a day. Their adult offspring then went through a series of tests designed to test anxiety-like behavior. Rats of stressed mothers avoided the open arms of the elevated plus maze. They also were more active during the tests in general, which could be an indication of escape behavior (Vallée et al., 1997). These results indicate a higher level of anxiety in the prenatally stressed rats than the non-stressed rats. This is further supported by the fact that the more active rats had higher levels of stress hormones than less active rats and rats that spent more time in the open arms had lower levels of stress hormones.

Anxious dogs may stay close to their family members or hide in unfamiliar places instead of exploring the area. Alternatively, they may show increased activity and have difficulty settling in new places. They may also be hyperaware of their surroundings (hypervigilant) and may react to sudden stimuli by barking or attempting to flee (increased startle).

Depression-like symptoms look a little different. One example of depression-like behaviors is learned helplessness. This occurs when an animal believes that their behavior has no impact on the events around them. Therefore, they won't make an attempt to escape a distressing experience, even when escape is possible. In the dog world, this is sometimes called "shutting down." Anhedonia, or the inability to experience pleasure, is another example of depression-like behavior. In rodents, this is often measured by a decrease in sugar water consumption. One possible sign of anhedonia in dogs, then, might be a decreased interest in food.

As further evidence of the similarities between humans and other animals, treatment with antidepressants and anti-anxiety medications commonly used in humans, will often decrease or eliminate these symptoms in nonhuman animals as well (Morley-Fletcher et al., 2003; Rayen et al., 2011; Cannas et al., 2014).

There is one more finding of the Vallée study that is worth mentioning here. This study also included a third group of rats. These rats were similar to the controls in that their mothers were not stressed during pregnancy. However, the third group also underwent handling shortly after birth. This handling involved picking up the pups and transferring them to another cage with their littermates for about 15 minutes each day for three weeks. The test results in this "handled" but not stressed group are very interesting. In contrast to the prenatally stressed offspring, the handled rats explored the open arms of the elevated plus maze. They also spent less time hiding in the corner during the open field test. These results suggest that handling shortly after birth may actually have a beneficial effect by reducing anxiety in new situations. I will discuss this in more detail in Chapter 5.

Very little research has been done on prenatal stress in dogs. One study was done on farmed blue foxes (Braastad et al., 1998). The researchers found that prenatally stressed foxes showed increased "behavioral reactivity," meaning that they were more active than controls. This manifested as more struggling while being held by a human and more activity during the open field test. They also found that the prenatally stress foxes had smaller adrenal glands and (in females) higher levels of stress hormones than the controls. Smaller adrenal glands are notable because the adrenal glands are involved in the production of stress hormones.

Prenatal stress impacts on health

Prenatal stress also causes physiological changes that can impact health down the road. Much of the research on health has focused on humans and there have been large-scale studies that have looked at this issue. Stress during pregnancy has been associated with dysregulation of the metabolic, endocrine and immune systems in the children (Entringer, 2008a and 2008b; Heim et al., 2000). These individuals had a higher body mass index, insulin resistance and increased risk for auto-immune disorders. Sound familiar? This relates back to the allostatic load theory that I discussed in Chapter 2. I could go on and on about the potential health impacts of prenatal stress (and stress later in life), but this book is focused on behavior and you have other things to do, so I will leave it at that.

Impacts of maternal stress on puppies

The impacts of prenatal stress can set the stage for behavior issues down the road. Puppies born to mothers that were stressed during pregnancy will be more prone to anxiety- and depression- like behaviors. If they learn to be afraid of something, it will likely be harder for them to recover from that initial learning (due to impaired extinction learning). They may also have deficits in social behavior. The research on social behavior has looked at behavior between animals of the *same* species. We cannot say with certainty that prenatal stress would impact dog behavior toward humans in the same way. However, given the close relationship between dogs and people, there is a good chance that social behavior towards humans is impacted in a similar way. This is an issue where it would be great to see more research. Finally, prenatal stress can impact the dog's physical health, which is a welfare issue as well.

The most obvious area of concern regarding prenatal stress in dogs is pregnant mothers in animal shelters. At the very least, the change in environment itself is a stressor. In addition, many of these dogs have already been living in a stressful environment prior to arriving at the shelter. For example, they may have been living in an unstable and unpredictable environment or suffering from poor nutrition or poor health. Puppies born to mothers living in poor breeding conditions (such as puppy mills) will also be subjected to prenatal stress. It is also important to recognize that even females from reputable breeder can experience stress during pregnancy. Unexpected circumstances, such as a major health issue in the mother or a house fire, can also lead to prenatal stress.

Animals that experience prenatal stress are at higher risk for health and behavior issues down the road. Recognizing this allows their caretakers to be proactive when working with such puppies—we will talk more about that in Chapters 5 and 6.

Puppy stress

Unfortunately, the prenatal period is not the only period where animals are vulnerable to the impacts of stress. Juvenile stress is usually referred to as "postnatal" stress in the scientific literature. It generally refers to the period after birth but before puberty or adolescence. In dogs, this most likely applies to the period from birth to about six months of age. Since many puppies are adopted at eight weeks of age or older, it's possible that puppies will be exposed to stress before coming to their permanent home. Of course, stress can occur after adoption as well. Toxic stress during this period of life can also have major impacts on behavior. This has many implications for how we raise puppies before and after they go to their new homes.

In humans, early life stress (generally abuse or neglect), is associated with the development of social anxiety, aggression and antisocial behavior in adolescents and adults (Roth et al., 2002; Veenema et al., 2006; Veenema, 2009; Bruce et al., 2012). In rodent studies, researchers have been able to isolate specific stressors and examine their impacts. We will look at these now. For clarification, "pup" refers to juvenile rodents and "puppy" refers to juvenile dogs.

Impacts of maternal separation on puppies

Much of the research at this age has focused on maternal care and maternal separation. It turns out separation and poor maternal care can have significant effects on development and behavior. In my example from before, a pregnant mom came into a shelter and was placed into foster care shortly after giving birth to her puppies. Although mom is now physically safe and receiving regular food and health care, she could still be stressed. She is in a new and unfamiliar place and she may be fearful of people, or unused to living in an indoor environment. If mom is emotionally stressed while caring for her puppies, that will likely also impact the puppies behavior. It's also not uncommon for puppies to be found without mom. In either case, these puppies are being hit twice. First, with chronic stress *in utero* and again during their first several weeks of life.

Activities such as grooming and nursing can help regulate physiological systems in the rat, including the HPA axis (Hofer, 1994). Even relatively short separations can have measurable impacts. A single 24-hour separation from mom can cause changes to stress responsiveness in rodents. The exact physiological effects vary depending on the age of separation as well as the sex of the offspring (Van Oers, de Kloet and Levine, 1998).

The mother rodent will naturally leave the nest for periods of 15 to 30 minutes at a time while she looks for food (Sánchez et al., 2001). This is a normal period of separation and is used as a control for comparing longer periods of separation—usually about three hours. These longer separations seem to negatively affect maternal care. Specifically, the mother is less responsive to the pups after separation (Huot et al., 1997). The pups themselves show increased levels of stress-related hormones (Huot et al., 1997). As adults, they are hyper-responsive to stress (Sánchez et al., 2001). That means they show increased levels of stress hormones in response to a stressor, and those reactions last longer. They also show increased anxiety- and depression-like behavior and increased anhedonia (decreased ability to experience pleasure) (Kalinichev et al., 2002; Sánchez et al., 2001). Many of the effects from maternal separation seen in rodents are also seen in primates, including increased fear and startle (Sánchez et al., 2005; Rosenblum et al., 2002). This tells us these effects are not limited to rodents, and likely occur in other mammals as well.

Early separation from mom and littermates (prior to natural weaning) can also lead to problems. At least in rodents, the stress axis is still developing prior to weaning so early stress causes changes to the stress response system (Stanton et al., 1998; Hennessy and Weinberg, 1990). In rodents, early separation is often linked to *lower* levels of stress hormones and an HPA axis that is *less* reactive to stress (Sandi and Haller, 2015). Having lower levels of stress hormones may seem beneficial. However, decreased stress responsiveness and lower stress hormone levels are still signs of dysregulation. Decreased responsiveness to stress has also been associated with trauma exposure and post-traumatic stress disorder in humans, though the results are inconsistent (Meewisse et al., 2007).

Unfortunately, there has been *very* little research done on development in dogs, but we have a few studies that may help. One study found that puppies separated from their mothers at six weeks were at higher risk for disease and even death than puppies weaned at 12 weeks (Slabbert and Rasa 1993). Another study compared puppies separated from their mothers at eight weeks with puppies separated between four and six weeks. The puppies separated between four and six weeks of age were more likely to display certain behavior issues, such as destructiveness, resource guarding, fear, and attention-seeking behaviors (Pierantoni et al., 2011). Puppies hand-reared until 3.5 weeks and then isolated until 12 weeks showed severe social deficits when interacting with other dogs (Fox and Stelzner, 1967). When puppies were instead raised by mom until 3.5 weeks and then isolated, the effects were less dramatic—some puppies showed deficits and others didn't. When the puppies were raised with mom until they were eight weeks old and then isolated until 12 weeks, they showed normal social behavior toward other dogs when tested at 12 weeks.

This tells us a few things about working with dogs. If mom is absent, it could have noticeable impacts on the puppies' behavior. We know from studies in other mammals that these impacts can be dramatic—they literally reorganize the brain and its circuits. This changes the behavioral and physiological response to stress and how they learn. Even small amounts of maternal care appear to have a positive impact. Therefore, we want to prevent maternal separation if possible. Allowing the mother to leave of her own accord is fine. What's important is avoiding forced separation. Practices like providing veterinary care for the mom in the living environment, rather than removing her for veterinary care, can help reduce separations.

Impacts on the quality of maternal care on puppies

As I mentioned above, we know that is not just separation that matters. The *quality* of maternal care is also important. Higher quality maternal care is associated with decreased stress reactivity (Liu et al., 1997). Research by Caldji et al. (1998, 2000) showed that offspring of rodent mothers with poor maternal care were less able in their ability to cope effectively with stress. This was shown as both behavioral and physiological changes. Animals that had poor maternal care may develop new fears more easily (Champagne et al., 2008). This is consistent with evidence that the offspring of rat mothers with poor quality maternal care show increased reactivity in the amygdala (Caldji et al., 1998). Increased *consistency* of high-quality maternal care is correlated with decreased stress reactivity (Akers et al., 2008). This may be related to predictability as a more predictable environment is less stressful. Taken together, these results tell us that poor quality maternal care can decrease an animal's ability to cope with stress.

This is one area where we have some research in dogs. It is clear that maternal care affects dog behavior, but the results are inconsistent. For example, Tiira and Lohi (2015) found higher levels of anxiety in dogs with less maternal care. However, a study on guide dog puppies found that puppies with higher levels of maternal care were less likely to succeed in the program (Bray et al., 2017).

Why are the results in the dog studies so inconsistent? There are several possible reasons. First, the puppies come from multiple different populations: working German Shepherds (Foyer et al., 2016), pet dogs (Guardini, 2017), guide dogs (Bray et al., 2017), and beagles in professional kennels (Guardini, 2016). (The guide dogs were a mix of German Shepherds, Golden Retrievers and Labrador Retrievers.) Three of these populations are dogs that are being purpose bred, which means they may have genetic differences that could interact with the effect of maternal care.

Second, in all of the studies, the maternal care was only observed for the first three weeks. That leaves no data for weeks four to eight. It is possible that the quality of maternal care could change as the puppies become more mobile. If that is the case, we would also need information on how much care the puppies are receiving during that period to make accurate predictions about their behavior. Also, in two of the studies, the puppies were tested at eight weeks of age. This may be too young for stress-related changes to show up based on what we know of the impacts of stress in juvenile rodents. Finally, there is some evidence that too *little* stress during development can also decrease stress resilience—more on that in Chapter 5.

Impacts of social isolation in puppies

Complete social isolation has even greater effects. Rhesus monkeys that experienced partial or complete social isolation at a young age had a long list of behavior issues (Harlow et al., 1965). They had severe social impairments and were not able to read social cues or form normal social relationships. They also showed increased levels of fear (Mason, 1960; Harlow et al., 1965) and impaired cognitive abilities, including decreased impulse control (Gluck and Sackett, 1976). Finally, isolated monkeys displayed increased anxiety (Sánchez et al., 2001). Longer periods of isolation caused increasingly dramatic and debilitating impacts and made them much more difficult, or impossible, to reverse. For the monkeys, six months appeared to be a major turning point, but remember that we cannot apply this timeline directly to dogs as their developmental trajectory is different. Certainly, the earlier the intervention in these cases, the better.

Rats, which are also a social species, are negatively impacted by social isolation as well. After isolation, they show depression-, anxiety-, and psychosis-like behaviors. Isolation also causes hormonal and neurological changes, including increased stress reactivity (Murínová et al., 2017; Mumtaz et al., 2018). There is very little research on social isolation during development in dogs, but one study found behavioral abnormalities and changes in the brain after only one week of isolation (Agrawal et al., 1976). Anecdotal evidence also suggests that isolation can have a profound impact on dog behavior, including increased fear and deficits in social skills.

In the case of social deprivation or other severe forms of neglect or abuse, there is evidence that the HPA axis may be blunted—these animals have lower levels of stress hormones than normal (Gunnar and Donzella, 2002; Lupien, et al., 2009). As I mentioned before, this still represents abnormal functioning and may be associated with decreased emotional health.

Adolescent stress

Kona was quite sick when she was just a few weeks old and almost died. However, she made a full recovery and grew into a very sweet puppy. She played nicely with the other dog in the household, excelled in puppy class and enjoyed interacting with people out in public. However, right around six months, things started to fall apart. She became extremely reactive on walks, barking and lunging so much the family could barely control her. She also started to get very difficult to manage in the home and would quickly escalate and start barking and mouthing—hard—if she didn't get her way. She also began to react fearfully to loud noises, something that hadn't seemed to bother her before. Her family was left wondering what had happened to their innocent little puppy. They even considered giving her back to the breeder as she was just too much to handle.

The period of adolescence is not well-defined in dogs, but it is generally considered to start around six months of age and continue until 12 to 18 months. In intact females, the onset is clearly defined as the age at first estrus. It is much more difficult to pinpoint the start of adolescence in males or in females that have been spayed prior to their first estrus.

Kona is not alone. Adolescence is a turbulent time. It appears to be an especially difficult period for dog-human relationships as shelters report being filled with adolescent dogs. Even dogs that stay in homes are often struggling. A very high proportion of my behavior calls come in for adolescent dogs. This is a quality-of-life issue for both the dogs and their families.

Much of the research on the impacts of chronic stress has focused on early development (prior to puberty). However, adolescence is a particularly interesting age regarding stress. Adolescence is often the period when early stressful experience begins to manifest into behavioral changes.

However, adolescence is also a period of critical brain, social, and emotional development (Lo Iacono and Carola, 2018) which makes it a period of vulnerability in its own right. In addition, adolescents (both humans and rodents) show a number of behavior changes including increased social interaction, arousal, impulsivity, interest in novelty, and risk-taking (Hueston et al., 2017; Lo Iacono and Carola, 2018). Given all of this, it's not surprising that adolescence is such a challenging time!

Impacts on stress response during adolescence

Compared to adults, the stress response in adolescent rats is delayed, but prolonged (Vazquez and Akil, 1993; Romeo, 2006). This means that stress hormones don't increase quite as quickly as in adults. However, once they increase, they stay higher longer. This may be because the negative-feedback system is still under development at this age (Goldman et al., 1973). In addition, healthy adults typically show habituation to repeated exposure to the same stressor—meaning their stress system doesn't respond as strongly after being exposed to the same stressor repeatedly (Girotti et al., 2006). However, in adolescents, you see the opposite effect. The response to repeated stressors increases over time (Romeo et al., 2006). Finally, adolescents that experienced early stress have higher baseline levels of stress hormones than those that did not (Evans and English, 2002; Halligan et al., 2007).

Impacts on anxiety- and depression-like behaviors during adolescence

In humans, toxic stress in adolescence is clearly linked to mental health issues later in life, including anxiety and depression (Andersen and Teicher, 2008: National Clearinghouse on Child Abuse and Neglect,

2005). Rats exposed to stress both during adolescence and again in adulthood, show increased anxiety- and depression-like behavior as adults (Tsoory et al., 2007). Rats raised in isolation during the adolescent period also show increased anxiety, fear and aggression (Burke et al., 2017). For example, they show increased fear of novel objects and unfamiliar environments (Einon and Morgan, 1977). They were also more fearful in social interactions (Lukkes et al., 2009). These effects can persist even if the animals are reintegrated at a later age (Lukkes et al., 2009; Wright et al., 1991). In fact, at least in rodents, the impact of social isolation during adolescence is greater than the impact of isolation at a younger age (Burke et al., 2017).

There is a critical point here that I want to make sure everyone understands. The stress research tells us that 1) adolescents are more vulnerable to stress; and 2) the impacts of earlier stress often show up during the adolescent period and persist into adulthood. This means that a puppy that undergoes stress during development and *seems behaviorally healthy at adoption* is still at high risk for behavior issues as they get older. This may be what happened with Kona. We *cannot* simply assess a puppy with a history of toxic stress, determine that they seem friendly and well-adjusted at the time, and leave it at that. That's not the end of the story! Puppies with a history of chronic or extreme developmental stress are at high risk for behavior issues later in life. That means if mom was stressed during pregnancy or if puppies experienced a lot of stress during early development, they are at risk of developing problems during adolescence.

If we want to reduce the risk of behavior issues and increase welfare and well-being in these dogs, then we need to face this issue directly. Adopters considering an adolescent dog should take into consideration the dog's history of developmental stress (if known). I believe that adopters need to be told that their puppies are at increased risk. There are ways of doing this without being overly alarmist or negative. For example, you might say "Fido had a rough start to life. That means he'll need extra support while he's growing to make sure that he learns the world is safe." We also need to tell adopters how to help their dogs. I would love to see shelters and rescues develop stress resilience programs for high-risk puppies that include adopter education as well as puppy socialization and skills classes. This applies to breeders as well. Even responsible breeders can't control for everything and there are times when their puppies may experience toxic stress later in life. Those dogs would benefit from extra help as well. Chapters 5 and 6 cover strategies for increasing stress resilience.

The other important point is that even an emotionally healthy dog is at increased risk during adolescence, simply because they are more vulnerable from a developmental standpoint. A dog that hasn't experienced toxic stress during early development can still react badly to stress during adolescence. That means we need to do what we can to build resilience from a young age and protect adolescents from toxic stress. Obviously, we want to do this for dogs at *any* age, but I point it out here because I think sometimes we focus on puppies so much that we do not realize adolescents may be just as vulnerable.

Impacts of lack of social interaction and play opportunities in adolescence

Social interaction at this age appears to be particularly important. Adolescent rats are more interested in social interaction than adults (Douglas et al., 2004; Yates et al., 2013). We just need to think back to our own adolescence to know that friends are critically important during this period for humans as well. Yet again, we don't have research on this in dogs, but, anecdotally it certainly appears that teenage dogs are more interested in socializing than most adults.

Rats that are isolated during adolescence react differently during encounters with unfamiliar adult rats. The adolescents display a high number of play behaviors toward the older rat and are less likely to display freezing behaviors even after being attacked multiple times (Burke et al., 2017). Andrew Burke and his colleagues (2017) have speculated that isolated rats are so motivated to interact with other rats, that being attacked is not as aversive as it would be in socialized rats!

Does this sound familiar to you at all? This immediately made me think of adolescent dogs that charge heedlessly up to other dogs and display repeated, over the top play behaviors. When they are rebuffed by the other dog—often quite strongly—they continue to try to interact, rather than retreating or toning down their intensity. I have seen young dogs like this provoke attacks because they are so unresponsive to another dog's social cues. I now wonder if this behavior is more likely in dogs that have not had enough social interaction with other dogs and if that social isolation is the cause of this maladaptive behavior. Perhaps their desire to interact is so strong that it persists even in the face of aggression. All these poor dogs want to do is make friends, but they are so socially inept that they end up making enemies and furthering their own social isolation!

One thing that seems to be particularly important in adolescences is play. Play appears to be important for the normal development of the brain and social behavior (Burke et al., 2017). Rats that were not able to play fight with age-matched peers at this age suffer from a number of negative effects. The effects include extreme defensiveness when approached by another rat, an inability to effectively diffuse conflict with other rats and decreased social interaction as adults (Hol et al., 1999; Pellis and Pellis, 2007; von Frijtag et al., 2002). Notably, these results were found even if the rats were raised with another individual that was not playful (Einon et al., 1978). In rats, at least, there is something critical about play with peers of similar age (Pellis and Pellis, 2007). Rats that are able to play as juveniles and adolescents are more adept at social interaction (Pellis et al., 2010).

Although we don't have research on the impacts of social play on development in dogs, these effects have been found in humans as well, suggesting that it's a shared trait among social mammals (Darwish et al., 2001). Several researchers have also suggested that play may help animals learn to cope with unpredictability and, by extension, to cope with stress (Held, 2017; Burke et al., 2017).

Stress in senior dogs

Seniors are the last group that is especially vulnerable to stress. Rats that are exposed to chronic stress show accelerated aging in the brain, including a decrease in the size of the hippocampus (important for memory) (Landfield et al., 1978; Landfield et al., 2007). Baseline stress hormone levels are also higher in human seniors diagnosed with Alzheimer's disease (Giubilei et al., 2001). Middle aged rats who were given artificial stress hormones for long periods of time showed a very similar pattern to naturally aged rats—a smaller hippocampus and memory impairments (Landfield et al., 1978; Issa et al., 1990). Conversely, middle aged rats whose stress hormone levels were kept artificially low using medications did not show memory loss or a decrease in the size of the hippocampus as they aged (Landfield et al., 1981). Taken together, this research suggests that stress hormones accelerate the process of age-related memory loss.

This means that minimizing stress in our older dogs is likely a key part of keeping them healthy. Think carefully before making any major life changes—including bringing in a new puppy—when you have an older dog. This is not to say that any change is bad or will have a negative impact. However, I recommend taking the potential impacts of stress into consideration when making decisions involving senior dogs. Chapter 6 will discuss what owners can do to develop and provide stress resilience in their dogs.

We have now covered the impacts of stress during the different phases of development. Next, we'll discuss how stress impacts learning and memory.

Chapter 4
How Toxic Stress Impacts Learning and Memory

Hank is an adorable black and tan hound mix. He was very uncomfortable around new people and would howl at them, then retreat and shake when they entered the house. His family hired a qualified behavior consultant and they have been working on teaching Hank that visitors predict hotdogs. Gradually, Hank's fear of strangers has been decreasing. A few days ago, Hank, who is also afraid of storms, was home alone during a terrible storm with strong winds and deafening thunder. His family came home to find him trembling under the bed. A few days later, they had visitors over and Hank's reaction to the visitors was stronger than it has been in months, taking everyone by surprise. What is going on here? Could Hank's thunderstorm experience impact his reaction to the strangers days later? This chapter is going to examine this question and more by discussing the relationship between stress and learning.

Dogs are good learners – for better or worse

One of the reasons that people have loved dogs ever since they were first domesticated is that they can learn behaviors so readily. They learn to read their owners; they learn that one thing leads to another. Pick up a dog's leash, he knows immediately that a walk is coming. They can also learn that a rolled-up newspaper may mean a swat on the rear is coming. As with the story of Hank above, they can link all kinds of things together, for better or worse.

Learning influences everything. Think of your personal life and how you've been shaped by your experiences. This goes well beyond book learning. Consider, for example, your pattern of personal relationships, your eating and exercise habits and your personal values. All these things are deeply influenced by learning. The same is true for our dogs. Learning is so much more than learning to behave appropriately in a human-centered world or learning the basics of agility. It includes how the dog responds to new experiences, how they make choices in their daily lives and how they interact with people and other dogs.

There are many different factors that shape behavior. However, learning is often one of the first things we think of when we consider influences on behavior. This is understandable as learning is one of the primary forces affecting behavior. Understanding how learning is impacted by stress will help you be more effective at changing behavior. Stress affects both classical and instrumental conditioning. Until recently, most of the research has focused on fear learning (one aspect of classical conditioning) and memory, rather than instrumental conditioning. However, there is some recent and very interesting work on instrumental learning that we'll discuss as well. We'll start with fear learning.

Fear learning

Scarlet was attacked by another dog as a puppy. Afterward, she was terrified of other dogs. This is known as **fear conditioning**. Fear conditioning is the process of learning to associate one thing (the conditioned stimulus) with something scary (the unconditioned stimulus). In this case, other dogs are the conditioned stimulus and the attack itself is the unconditioned stimulus. Put another way, Scarlet had developed a conditioned fear of other dogs.

Over time, Scarlet saw many dogs at a comfortable distance and was not attacked. Eventually her fear diminished. This is known as **fear extinction**. It refers to the process of learning that a particular stimulus (other dogs) no longer predicts a bad experience (being attacked). Being able to undergo fear extinction is important for the welfare of our dogs because it allows them to recover from scary experiences. However, not all animals undergo fear conditioning and extinction at the same rate.

Stress impacts both fear conditioning and fear extinction. Stressed animals can become sensitized to fear. Compared to unstressed animals, animals that have recently experienced stress develop conditioned fear more quickly. That conditioned fear is also stronger in recently stressed animals. The maximum time period that can elapse between an initial stressor and the development of conditioned fears, whether to that stressor or other stressors, is unclear, but current evidence shows that animals can remain sensitized for at least a week (Rau et al., 2005; Schmeltzer, 2015). This may not seem like much, but it becomes especially sobering when you consider that some animals are experiencing stress on a regular basis. It's also possible that effect lasts much longer. Individuals with post-traumatic stress disorder often remain sensitized to stress for much longer than seven days. The length of the effect may vary depending on what stage of development the animal was in when they experienced the stress. Remember, for example, that juveniles and adolescents seem to be particularly vulnerable to stress.

Unfortunately, most of these studies take the following format. The animal is exposed to stress for some period of time—hours or days depending on if the study is looking at acute or chronic stress. The animal then has a "rest" period of one to seven days where they are not stressed. After the rest period, the animal is again exposed to stress—usually a different type of stress in a different context. The results of these studies show that animals exposed to stress within the last week show stronger fear conditioning than those not exposed to stress (Cordero et al., 2003; Rau et al., 2005). This is often accompanied by changes to the brain or HPA activity (Cordero et al., 2003). There is also evidence that prior stress can enhance **fear recall**—that is, once the animal has been stressed, they more readily remember previous fear learning (McGuire et al., 2010). Again, this effect was found even after a delay of one week. These phenomena are thought to be important factors in the development of PTSD in humans.

Clients will sometimes ask me if a dog's stressful experience a week ago (like the thunderstorm Hank experienced in the story above) explains why the dog had a particularly strong negative reaction to something today. I used to say, "probably not." However, now that I am more familiar with this research, I do think it's possible—even likely—that experiences from several days to a week ago (possibly even longer) may influence current behavior. It is clear that if the dog was attacked by another dog last week, they may be more afraid of other dogs today. But this research is different in that it focuses on a different type of stress and a different location from the initial location. In the case of Hank, he experienced a thunderstorm that caused him to react more strongly to a visitor several days later.

That means it's not just simple classical conditioning. Something else is going on here. The research suggests that toxic stress may cause a general sensitization to future stressors. Rodent studies show that this effect lasts at least a week, but it could be longer, we just do not have data on that yet.

Extinction of fear

Remember that stress damages the hippocampus. The hippocampus plays an important role in extinction learning. There is evidence that damage to the hippocampus can lead to impaired extinction learning (Maren, 2011). Indeed, when animals are stressed, it is harder to extinguish their fear (Hartley et al., 2014; Izquierdo et al., 2006; Miracle et al., 2006). Stress also makes extinction less likely to stay in place once it has been acquired (Knox et al., 2012). In practical terms, you tend to see this manifest in two ways—either you will see less of a reduction of fear in the first place or you will see a stronger return of the fear over time.

Let's return to the example of Scarlet. If Scarlet is under a lot of stress, then she is going to have a more difficult time letting go of her association with other dogs and being attacked. She will not be able to make as much progress as she would if she were not stressed. In addition, if her fear does decrease, that improvement will be less stable if she is stressed. Extinction tends to be unstable anyway and fear tends to return in a variety of situations, but the process is likely to be accelerated in dogs that are experiencing stress. Essentially, toxic stress makes it harder to reduce fear in dogs.

There are many different things that may cause distress in dogs. If a dog is under chronic stress, it's best to work on reducing that distress before starting a behavior modification plan. Strategies for decreasing stress and fear are discussed in Chapter 6.

Prenatal stress also seems to interfere with the process of fear extinction. In a study by Green et al. (2011), female rats experienced one hour of stress each day during their last week of pregnancy. Their adult male offspring were then subjected to both chronic and acute stress. Examples of the stressors used in this study are swimming in cold water and losing a fight over a resource against another rat. While certainly unpleasant, these are not extreme events and are not unlike the types of stressors pet dogs might face. The study found that the rats that experienced prenatal stress while *in utero* had higher levels of stress hormones and changes in brain areas related to extinction and emotional regulation when compared to those whose mothers were not stressed. Extinction was not as effective in rats that experienced prenatal stress *and* stress as adults compared to those that only experienced stress as adults. Similar results have been found in other studies (Maren and Holmes, 2016; Wilson et al., 2013). This is yet another way that prenatal stress makes animals more vulnerable. For adolescents, the picture is less clear. Some studies in rodents have shown that adolescents do not seem to respond to extinction as well as adults (Hefner and Holmes, 2007; Pattwell et al., 2012). Adults that were stressed during adolescence also did not respond as well to extinction (Ishikawa et al., 2012; Judo et al., 2010). However, another study showed that acute stress may aid extinction in adolescents (Schayek and Maroun, 2014).

When evidence is unclear, as it is in this case, it often means that the exact effect of the stress varies according to a variety of factors. The impact of stress on extinction learning in adolescents may vary according to the exact type and timing of the stressor, for example (Maren and Holmes, 2016). There is also some evidence that the effectiveness of extinction depends on genetics. One study found the heritability of extinction effectiveness was greater than 33% (Shumake et al., 2014). More research will be needed before we can get a clear picture of exactly how stress impacts extinction learning in adolescents.

Trauma and PTSD

Any discussion on the impacts of stress and learning would be incomplete without a discussion of **trauma**. The definition of trauma is a bit tricky. Frank McMillan (2020) points out that there are two definitions of trauma. The first occurs when an individual experiences or witnesses an extremely distressing event. The second definition relates to how the individuals *responds* to experiencing or witnessing the event. This is an important distinction because not all individuals respond to trauma in the same way. McMillan chooses to refer to the events themselves as "potentially traumatic events" and to the animals' response as trauma. That is the approach I will take in this book as well.

Trauma occurs in response to a very intensely distressing experience. For example, a threat or perceived threat to one's life or severe emotional distress. In the case of trauma, the experience does not need to be chronic to qualify as toxic—it can happen with acute stress as well. It's the animal's perception of the experience that determines whether or not an event was traumatic.

The impacts of trauma occur along a continuum. Many individuals show signs of distress and impairment immediately after the traumatic event. However, most individuals recover within the weeks following the event. A certain percentage of people continue to show distress and functional impairments for a longer period of time. This can manifest in a number of different ways, many of which are consistent with the impacts of toxic stress that we have already discussed.

Perhaps the most severe form of trauma response in people is **post-traumatic stress disorder (PTSD)**. The primary effect of PTSD is a generalized and persistent fear response, even outside the context of the original trauma. However, it has several other impacts as well. The DSM-V (American Psychiatric Association, 2013) lists the following four categories of symptoms:

- Intrusions—this includes nightmares, flashbacks and physiological responses to trauma-related triggers
- Avoidance of trauma-related stimuli
- Changes to cognition and mood
- Changes to arousal and reactivity

Do dogs experience PTSD? That is a very complicated question. The first issue that needs to be addressed is whether or not dogs experience similar symptoms. In order to do that, we'll need to look at each list of categories in more detail. Be aware that people do not need to show every single one of these symptoms to receive a diagnosis of PTSD. Rather, they only need to display one or two symptoms of each *category*. Also, not everyone who experiences trauma develops PTSD.

As mentioned above, intrusions often involve repeated re-experiencing of the traumatic event. Individuals are transported back into the moment of trauma and respond as if they are in that moment again. We have no way of knowing if nonhuman animals experience nightmares or flashbacks. However, we can measure and observe physiological and behavioral responses to trauma-related triggers. Many studies in rodents have utilized conditioned fear responses as a model for PTSD and it's clear that rodents have physiological responses as a result of distressing experiences.

Furthermore, many scientists believe that PTSD involves an impairment of extinction (VanElzakker et al., 2014). That would explain why the intrusions continue even in the absence of continued traumatic events. Normally, if an individual repeatedly experiences a stimulus associated with an aversive stimulus *without* the aversive stimulus, the fear response will decrease. This does not happen in PTSD, indicating that something has gone wrong with the extinction process. This is something that is also seen in animal models of PTSD (Singewald and Holmes, 2019). So, evidence suggests that dogs can experience extinction-resistant physiological responses to trauma-related cues.

One of the roles of the prefrontal cortex is to aid in the inhibition of the fear memories by sending signals to the amygdala (Fenster, 2018). If the prefrontal cortex is not working well, it's less able to hold back those old fear memories. Researchers believe this is one reason that extinction is less stable in animals suffering from post-traumatic stress (Fenster, 2018).

Also remember that when the hippocampus is impaired, which is often the case in trauma victims, animals have a more difficult time distinguishing between safe and unsafe contexts. This can lead to generalized anxiety and fear, even outside of the original trauma-related stimuli.

Because trauma-related stimuli trigger intrusions, people with PTSD often go to great lengths to avoid stimuli related to the traumatic experience or experiences. Avoidance is problematic because it prevents the animal from going through the process of extinction. If you never actually experience the scary thing, you don't have the opportunity to learn that you can tolerate the scary thing and still be okay. Therefore, avoidance is considered a major issue in PTSD and one of the primary factors that perpetuates the fear (Paredes and Morilak, 2019). Again, we can't know if other animals experience intrusions. However, avoidance behavior is something that has also been observed in animal models of PTSD (Singewald and Holmes, 2019), as well as anecdotally in my work with dogs. I think it's safe to conclude that dogs experience avoidance.

The next category of symptoms includes changes to mood and cognition. People with PTSD often experience persistent negative mood. Researchers believe this is due in part to emotional dysregulation which makes it difficult for people to control their emotions (Fenster et al., 2018). In a normal, healthy brain, certain brain areas play an important role in inhibiting the strength of emotions. Those brain areas are not functioning properly in individuals with PTSD, leading to intense and overwhelming emotions (Fenster et al., 2018). People with PTSD also seem to be less able to process rewards and are often unable to experience pleasure. Animal models have demonstrated that animals also show an increased negative mood and a decreased ability to experience pleasure (Deslauriers et al., 2018). Based on my own work with dogs, I feel that animals also experience emotional dysregulation, though in most cases, I don't have enough information on the history of the dog to say if this emotional regulation is due to trauma, or some other factor.

Cognitive changes include decreased attention, impulse control and behavioral flexibility. The decreased behavioral flexibility means that people may struggle to adjust their response as needed to fit the situation. Rats under stress have also shown changes in cognition (Deslauriers et al., 2018).

Taken together, research suggests that nonhuman animals can also show changes to cognition and mood as a result of intensely distressing experiences.

The final category is changes to arousal and reactivity. This category includes a long list of issues such as hypervigilance, increased startle, irritability and increased reactive aggression (defensive behavior). Again, animal models have found similar responses in nonhuman animals (Fenster et al., 2018).

In summary, although we cannot speak to every symptom of PTSD in humans, nonhuman animals do seem to show symptoms from each of the four categories of PTSD symptoms. Interestingly, PTSD animal models also produce long-lasting trauma-related symptoms at about the same rate as PTSD in humans—about 25% (McMillan, 2020). (Though, it's worth noting that the incidence of PTSD after trauma can vary widely depending on the population). Based on this information, I think it's safe to say that dogs can experience long-term distress as a result of severely distressing experiences. This is not the end of the story, however.

Next, we can ask ourselves if the dog experience is enough like the human experience to be considered PTSD in the human sense of the word. I think we need to be extremely cautious with this. We cannot truly know that the symptoms we are seeing are a direct result of trauma. In many cases, we don't have enough information on the background of the dog to know they have experienced trauma. In these cases, it's impossible to determine if a dog's behavior is attributable to previous trauma. There are other things that can cause PTSD symptoms including chronic stress during development. Even if we do know of previous trauma, we cannot say for sure that the behavior is due to that trauma, particularly if the behavior is delayed or global in scope. There are cases when a specific incident happens and results in a very clear trajectory of behavior change that is almost certainly linked to the aversive experience. However, in my experience in working with dogs, that specific situation is quite rare compared to dogs that come in with an incomplete history or no clearly identifiable traumatic experience.

In addition, we do not know what a dog's inner experience is like. Although there are many consistencies in physiology and behavior across animals, each species is still unique and has a variety of species-specific characteristics that will influence their perception of the world and their behavior. If we assume the dog experience is exactly like the human experience, we run into the danger of denying dogs the characteristics that make them unique. This, then, may impair our ability to appropriately address their unique experience and, in turn, impair our ability to most effectively help *them*. Researchers are fond of using terms like "depression-like" or "PTSD-like." This may seem to deny animals the full human experience, but I tend to think of it as respecting that their world is different from ours and reminding ourselves to honor those differences. Using a term such as PTSD-like does not deny that an animal is experiencing extreme-suffering. It simply acknowledges that the experience of a dog, for example, is not going to be an exact duplicate of the experience of a human.

This brings us to the last question. Is there an advantage to diagnosing dogs with PTSD (or PTSD-like symptoms)? What do we gain from labeling dogs with PTSD (or PTSD-like behavior)? Does using that terminology somehow allow us to treat a dog more effectively? I don't see how it does. In fact, it could lead to confusion or increased distressed on the part of their guardian. I think it makes more sense to focus on the behavioral symptoms and address them, rather than giving a dog a diagnosis. That doesn't mean we cannot acknowledge the potential role of trauma—or chronic stress—I simply don't think the advantages of using PTSD outweigh the potential costs. It's also worth noting that in many places veterinarians are the only professionals permitted to make diagnoses.

Addressing for trauma and PTSD-like symptoms

What *can* we do with this information? First, I think it is important to be aware of how globally trauma and toxic stress can impact behavior. If you are living or working with a dog that is showing PTSD-like symptoms, that serves as a red flag to check for other symptoms that may also be present. For example, is a dog showing persistent fear? Perhaps we should also assess them for avoidance, hypervigilance and a decreased ability to feel pleasure. Then we can create a comprehensive behavior modification plan that addresses all the issues, instead of just focusing on fear. This is also true if the dog is not responding well to training—perhaps there are other aspects of behavior that need to be addressed.

A full description of how to treat fear and aggression is beyond the scope of this book. However, I will give you a few things that you can do to address some of the symptoms of trauma exposure. Many of the first-line treatment approaches for PTSD in people include some kind of exposure therapy. This therapy is aimed at addressing the issue of avoidance and teaching individuals that they can face the trauma-related stimuli. By addressing the avoidance, extinction is able to occur, and the fear can diminish.

Exposure therapy involves exposing the individual to the aversive stimuli and helping them tolerate the distressing emotions that arise. A key component of this type of therapy is that the individual is a willing participant. They understand why they are going through the process and have the freedom to opt out at any point. Without the ability to willingly engage in the process and opt out at any time, exposure therapy essentially becomes flooding which is *not* a recommended treatment for fear or anxiety. In the past, I have said that exposure therapy cannot be used with dogs for this reason. However, more recently it has occurred to me that a technique I have been using for some time may mimic the process of exposure therapy in humans.

When I have a dog that is fearful of inanimate objects, I will often shape them to touch and interact with that object. Sometimes it is a specific fear of a particular thing, but much more often that dog is generally afraid of anything new or unusual. I place the item in an open area and start by reinforcing with food if the dog looks at or moves toward the item. Typically, I throw the food behind the dog so there is no pressure for the dog to approach the object in order to get the food. Once the dog is consistently looking at the object, I wait for any kind of movement toward the object, again rewarding behind the dog. Finally, they are reinforced with a treat for touching the item with a paw or nose. Throughout this process, I simply observe the dog and reinforce through praise and food when they make progress. I do not encourage them in any way. That includes calling them to me, trying to lure with food or using the leash to apply pressure or prevent retreat. I have found that even mild forms of attempted encouragement often appear to increase stress on the dog and either slow down the process or cause the dog to completely shut down. Instead, I simply wait for them to be ready and then reinforce choices I like. I also keep these sessions very short in the beginning—less than five minutes, and often less than that.

Once the dog is confident with one item, I introduce a new item. It's not unusual for dogs to eventually start to approach novel objects on their own in anticipation of a treat. This is truly an amazing process to watch and one of the most rewarding behavior modification techniques that I use.

Now let's think of this in terms of exposure therapy. Remember, the point of exposure therapy is to address the issue of avoidance, which is preventing fear from going through the process of extinction. If a dog is avoiding novel objects because they elicit fear, then the dog never has an opportunity to learn that the novel object is safe. That means they are walking around in a world where every new or unusual object is a potential source of distress. By reinforcing the dog for looking at, approaching, and interacting with the item, they are able to learn that the item is not, in fact, dangerous. This allows for the process of fear extinction. Adding food accelerates the process of extinction by also associating the items with something enjoyable (counter conditioning for those of you in the know). Finally, the dog has control. They can leave at any time. In Chapters 5 and 6, you will learn all about the benefits of control.

Essentially, this process accomplishes three things:

1. Extinction => reduces fear
2. Association of scary thing with something good => increases positive emotions
3. Increased control => improves ability to cope with stress

The one thing that is missing is being able to explain to the dog *why* we are playing this game, but perhaps that's not essential if they have the ability to leave at any time. Note that I *do not* do this activity with unfamiliar people or other dogs. They are too dynamic and unpredictable and the likelihood of something scary or threatening happening is too high. I *may* do this with someone that the dog lives with and is afraid to interact with if there is no history of aggression (or likely aggression) and I trust the person to carefully follow the rules. This is not something you should attempt with people (or dogs) unless you are already experienced in working with dogs that have a history of fear and aggression toward people and/or dogs.

Another common technique that I really like is quite similar. This involves teaching a hypervigilant dog to offer eye contact in new environments. In this case, I generally start with teaching the behavior in a familiar environment. My goal is for the dog to *offer* eye contact without being prompted. Again, I shape this behavior by waiting for the dog to glance at me and reinforcing that behavior. In some cases, if looking at me is too hard, I will reinforce a head turn or ear flick. Once eye contact in a familiar place is easy and consistent, I will move to a quiet, unfamiliar location and repeat the process. The idea is to address the hypervigilance before trying to teach the dog other behaviors as being in a state of hypervigilance will work against you when trying to introduce a new behavior.

Stress and memory

There is ample evidence that stress affects memory. But it turns out that exactly how stress impacts memory is extremely complicated. To be honest, it's confusing. I will do my best to clearly lay out what we know, without oversimplifying the relationship between stress and memory. The first thing to understand is that there are several different processes involved in memory and stress impacts each of them somewhat differently. First, information in short-term memory is transferred to long-term memory. This is called **encoding**. When this information is first transferred, the memory is vulnerable to being lost or altered before it is stabilized. Once the memory is transferred, it needs to be retained. It can then be retrieved for use later on. Unsurprisingly, this is called **retrieval**! Finally, after retrieval, the memory goes through another period of vulnerability before it is **reconsolidated**. You may be starting to see why the impacts of stress on memory are so complicated. There are many different points along the process and stress does not impact all of them equally!

The other thing to remember is that stress is adaptive. That is, it serves a function that helps the animal survive. Therefore, it makes sense to assume that the interaction between stress and memory should also be adaptive in healthy animals. In animals that have already been damaged by stress, the impact on learning may no longer be adaptive—at least not once they are living in a safe and stable environment. The continuation of the negative impacts of stress, even after the initial stressors have stopped, leads to stress-related behavioral disorders.

Stress that occurs just before or during learning (encoding) has differing effects on memory—sometimes it enhances it and sometimes it impairs it (Elzinga et al., 2005; Payne et al., 2006; Schwabe et al., 2008). Scientists are still in the process of determining why we see different results. One thing that seems clear is that memory of *emotional* experiences is enhanced by stress.

This was first discovered through a set of classic studies by Cahill and colleagues (Cahill et al., 1995; Cahill and McGaugh, 1995). In these studies, participants were shown a series of pictures accompanied by a story. One story portrayed an emotional narrative where a young boy is hit by a car and critically wounded (emotional story). Another story—using the same photographs—tells the story of the boy observing an emergency disaster drill at the hospital (non-emotional story). After a couple of weeks, subjects were shown the photos again and asked to recall the details of the story. Those that listened to the emotional story recalled more details than those that listened to the less emotional story.

Stress also seems to enhance the memory of information relevant to coping with the stressor itself (Shields et al., 2017). This has been shown in research on rats using the Morris Water maze. In this test a rat is placed in a tank of water. Somewhere in the tank, there is a submerged platform the rat can stand on. Because it is slightly under water, the rat cannot see the platform. The job of the rats is to find the platform by swimming around until they come across it. Researchers can then test how well the rat remembers the location of the platform in subsequence tests. Finding this platform means the rat has a safe, stable place to rest. Therefore, remembering the location of the platform directly relates to coping with the stressor. Several studies have shown that if the water in the tank is very cold (a stressor), the rats will be better at remembering its location in subsequent tests than rats that performed the test in water that was not uncomfortably cold (Sandi et al., 1997; Joëls, 2006). Being stressed helped the rat remember the location of the platform, because it's relevant to helping them escape the stressor.

Think about this in a dog training context. A nervous dog goes to a group class and is overwhelmed by the other dogs. If they get too close, she barks and lunges. The trainer is able to keep her far enough from the other dogs that she is not barking and lunging. She remains nervous but can go through many of the steps of training and seems to be learning some of the cued behaviors taught in class. However, the research by Cahill and others suggests that she *may* be retaining more about her emotional experience (anxiety and distress) than the training cues we are trying to teach her. I emphasize the word 'may' here because it's difficult to know how well remembering details from a story or spatial memory of a platform translates to instrumental learning. This is an area where we really need some new studies that directly address the impact of stress in a training context!

Stress just *after* encoding appears to enhance memory (Preuss and Wolf, 2009; Beckner et al., 2006; Shields et al., 2017). However, this is only the case if the stressor occurs in the same location where the encoding happened. If the animal is moved to a different location, and is stressed in that location, there is no enhancing effect.

Valenchon et al. (2013) subjected horses to stress either just before or just after learning to touch a cone. The stress exposure lasted for 30 minutes and consisted of a variety of stressors, including loud sounds, shaking a tarp and spraying the horse with water. The horses were stressed in a different location from where the training session occurred. A third group of horses was not exposed to any stressor. Eight days later, all the horses went through another session of teaching them to touch a cone.

Horses that were stressed before or after the first learning session did not show any significant improvement between the first and second sessions. This suggests that learning was *not* enhanced by stress around the time of initial learning. This makes sense because the stress and the training happened in two different locations. Events that happen in the same location as the stressor are more likely to be relevant to the stressor itself than events that happen in a totally different context from the stressor.

Generally, stress has a negative impact on retrieval (Buchanan et al., 2006; Schwabe and Wolf 2009; Shields et al., 2017). For example, in a study by Merz et al. (2010), study participants were brought into the lab and asked to review and try to remember biographical information (encoding). After this, they were informed that they would have to give a speech on an unknown topic (the stressor). After the speech, they were asked to recall the biographical information they learned earlier.

How did the stress impact memory? Individuals that were stressed (those that gave the speech) made more errors in recall than those that did not give the speech. In addition, there was a correlation between the increase in stress hormones and memory retrieval—stronger stress hormone responses meant decreased memory retrieval. Put simply, if people are stressed, it is harder for them to remember previously learned information. Most of the studies in this area are similar to the speech study. They focus on the impact of stress on memorizing and recalling things like lists of words, or biographical information about an unfamiliar person. It is difficult to predict how this type of verbal memory and processing translates into our work with dogs.

In addition, we know that people are more likely to recall memories that match their current emotional state (Bower 1981; Klaassen et al., 2002). If someone is feeling positive emotions, they are more likely to recall a positive memory. If they are feeling a negative emotion, such as fear, they are more likely to recall a negative memory. This is called mood-congruent memory. There is some evidence of mood-congruent memory in nonhuman animals as well (Burman and Mendl, 2018). In this way, distress can impact not only how much an animal remembers, but what kinds of things they remember.

Why does the exact timing of stress matter so much? I mentioned earlier that stress is adaptive. It follows that the impacts of stress on memory should also be adaptive. Stress before encoding may or may not enhance memory. Stress just after encoding tends to enhance memory. Researchers believe that stress enhances memory when it is relevant to the learning—that is, the context and timing of the stress matches up with the learning. However, when stress occurs outside of the context of learning, it tends to impair memory (Schwabe and Wolf, 2010). Think about it. Imagine you are walking down the street. You hear a loud honk and immediately afterwards are almost hit by a blue truck. Which are you more likely to remember? The loud blast of the horn or the color of the truck? Which is more relevant to survival? It makes much more sense for us to remember the loud honk than the color of the truck.

This all makes perfect sense from a survival standpoint. Remembering insignificant details will not help us survive future threats. I used a human example here because it can be easier for us to relate. But all of this applies to our dogs as well.

This makes sense in terms of mood-congruent memory as well. If you are feeling particularly fearful, it's much more adaptive to pull up other memories related to fear. They are more likely to be able to help you in that moment than positive memories. When we think of this in modern life, it may not seem helpful. If you're feeling sad, wouldn't it be nice to suddenly be flooded with good memories? Of course! However, if we think back to how animals have evolved, we can see that mood-congruent memory is likely to aid in survival. If an animal is feeling fearful in the wild, it's likely because there is a threat to survival and, therefore, pulling up memories of other scary experiences is more likely to be helpful than memories of, say, basking in the sun.

All of this suggests that dogs are most likely to remember things they associate with a stressful experience. If we are trying to teach a dog something that is irrelevant to their emotional experience in that moment (or just before or after that moment), it's likely going to be difficult to make much progress. It also tells us that if we've done work in one context with a dog, that expecting them to remember that work when they are actively scared (especially if the context has changed) may be unrealistic.

I made this mistake once with my own dog Finn. He has had a lot of health issues and despite my best efforts, he is not a fan of the vet. When the pandemic hit and we could no longer enter the veterinary clinic with our dogs, I switched him to a clinic that was Fear-Free certified (my previous clinic had not been). I had worked on muzzle training him at home and at his original vet clinic. He likes his muzzle and is always happy to put it on and wear it. He had never been muzzled against his will and, as such, didn't have any negative associations with it. When we arrived at the new clinic (where he had never been), I muzzled him and then attempted to hand the leash to the technician. He immediately panicked and started trying to escape the muzzle. I'm sure there are many reasons for this, but one of them is likely that the impacts of stress on memory interfered with his ability to effectively recall the muzzle training work that we had done previously in a different context.

By the way, things turned out okay for Finn. Our new veterinarian is wonderful and came outside to examine him so I could stay with him. Since then he's had several happy visits and one of Finn's best friends (my former intern and sometimes dog sitter) now works at his new clinic, so the experience has become much less stressful for him since the first visit!

Note that there are different types of memory. The research above focuses on aspects of episodic memory. It does not necessarily apply to aspects of skill learning, such as teaching our dogs to sit and stay on cue or perform agility and obedience exercises. However, more recently, there has been a growing interest in the effect of stress on instrumental behaviors. That's what we will cover next.

Stress and habit

So far, we have been looking at how stress impacts the quantity of information retained. However, there is another important factor—the quality of memory retained. This is where we start to get solidly into the realm of instrumental conditioning. Many of you are probably familiar with the different types of instrumental conditioning: positive and negative reinforcement and punishment. But it turns out that instrumental conditioning also involves two different processes: stimulus-response and action-outcome.

I will start with action-outcome learning because that is probably what's most familiar to most of the readers. **Action-outcome** learning refers to the development of a causal relationship between a particular action (the behavior) and a particular outcome (the reinforcer or punisher). For example, a dog learns that sitting results in cheese. If the action-outcome relationship changes, then the behavior also changes. That is, if the dog sits and does *not* get cheese, then the behavior of sitting should decrease. In other words, the behavior is flexible. This type of learning is also often referred to as goal-directed behavior because the animal is intentionally engaging in the behavior in order to receive the reinforcement. (Dickinson, 1985; Balleine and Dickinson 1998; Schwabe and Wolf, 2010). When someone learns a new skill or practices active problem solving, they are engaged in goal-directed behavior.

However, some memories involve the development of a relationship between a stimulus and response. In this case the stimulus (cue) becomes associated with a particular response (behavior). For this reason, this type of learning is called **stimulus-response** learning. These memories are more rigid. They are more resistant to extinction. That means that if the relationship between the behavior and the outcome changes, the behavior is likely to continue. In this case, if the dog sits and doesn't get cheese, they keep sitting anyway. This is habit! Habits form when a particular stimulus-response-sequence is repeated over and over again in the same context. The relationship between the stimulus and the response becomes so strong that when the stimulus is presented, the animal produces the response automatically—without the involvement of intention! We know that habit and goal-directed behavior are two different types of memory because they are processed in two different brain areas!

It turns out that stress impacts which memory system we tend to rely on. Under conditions of stress, animals switch to more habitual behaviors (Wirz et al., 2018). That means they move from more intentional, flexible and goal-directed behaviors to more automatic, rigid and habitual behaviors. Habit memory is also more resistant to extinction than cognitive memory (Valentin et al., 2007).

The implications of this shift for training and behavior modification are quite large. Think about this in your own life. How many times have you reverted to habitual behavior when you're stressed? Maybe you have successfully been eating healthier recently, but then you have a bad day and habitually reach for the chocolate in your cabinet. Or perhaps you're running late for an appointment and habitually take the shortest route even though you *know it's closed due to construction!* Now you're running even later! Those are human examples, but what might this look like in our dogs?

Think of the reactive dog. They've been going through a process of behavior modification and are doing much better, but then they become startled by a dog that appears suddenly and completely lose their mind. Now the rest of the walk is shot. Why? One part of the explanation is that the dog is now stressed and, therefore, they revert to the behavior that's been rehearsed over and over again. In this case, that's the stimulus-response pattern of "see dog=>bark/lunge." This may also explain why it's so incredibly difficult to get their attention once they are barking and lunging—they are now living in their stress brain where habit reigns and the thinking part is not activated. This is why frequently practicing the behavior that we want—heeling or eye contact, for example—is so critically important to success when working with reactive dogs. We want *those* behaviors to become so well-rehearsed that they become habitual and replace the bark/lunge habit. Another tactic is to start working on the behavior in a different environment. Because habit is driven by environmental cues, changing to a new context can make the behavior more flexible and less habitual. In other words, it should be easier to change.

Another example is the performance dog that develops a bad habit in training. Let's say you have an obedience dog with crooked sits. After the pattern has developed, you spend a lot of time retraining for beautiful straight sits. And it works! Your dog now consistently sits straight at your side in heel position. You now return to the show ring and what do you get? Crooked sits! One reason for this is likely that the dog is now experiencing stress and, therefore, reverting to their original habit!

Chapter summary

Stress has a number of negative impacts on learning and memory. Stress can sensitize animals to future fear learning, making it easier for them to acquire new fears and resulting in new fears that are stronger than they would be in animals that had not been recently stressed. These effects can last at least a week past the initial stressor. In addition, stress makes already learned fear more resistant to extinction. Taken together, this means that dogs that are stressed are more vulnerable to developing fears and will likely be more difficult to treat for existing fears.

In addition, stress has a number of impacts on memory. The effects of stress on encoding new memories varies, but in general, stress appears to aid in the memory of emotional events and events related to the stressor. Finally, stress causes animals to move from more cognitive, goal-directed and flexible behavior to more automatic, habitual and rigid behavior.

In sum, minimizing stress is critically important if we want to maximize our dogs' well-being as well as their ability to learn what we want them to learn.

Chapter 5
Why are Some Dogs More Resilient to Stress Than Others?

We all know people who have been through terrible experiences and yet seem to be doing well in life. We know others who do not cope well at all and are facing serious mental health issues, substance abuse or other stress-related issues. The same is true for dogs. Some dogs seem to be relatively unphased by stress while other dogs fall to pieces at the smallest provocation. Of course, what we hope for is the former—dogs who are able to experience stressful events with little to no long-term negative consequences. This is known as **resilience**. My favorite definition of resilience is "achieving a positive outcome in the face of adversity" (McEwen, 2015).

Scientists are only just beginning to understand why some individuals are more resilient than others. Researchers Schiele and Domschke emphasize that the study of resiliency is still "in infancy" (2018). Keep this in mind as you read through this chapter. I'll be discussing what we think may be going on—but we do not have this fully worked out yet! Up until recently, researchers thought resilience was a passive process—either someone had it, or they did not (Brachman et al., 2015). However, there is now growing evidence that resilience is an active process. That means that there are things we can do to influence resilience, which is excellent news for working with dogs! The factors that will be explored in this chapter are:

- Genetics and epigenetics
- Personality and coping styles
- Early life experiences

- The opportunity for the dog to exert control
- The intensity and predictability of stressors

Genetics and epigenetics

The first thing we are going to look at is genetics. Researchers are beginning to find evidence that genetics does influence resilience. Some of this comes from looking at resilience in general and some of it is specific to stress-related mental health conditions such as PTSD and depression. So far, it appears there are several ways in which genetics may affect stress resilience.

First, genetics may influence differences in reactivity of the sympathetic nervous system. Remember, the sympathetic nervous system is the system involved in the fast-acting stress response. It causes the immediate fight-or-flight response and releases epinephrine and norepinephrine. Finley et al. (2004) found that people with a particular gene variant had a stronger response to stress than those without the variant. Consider two dogs and their reaction to guests. One dog may be excited and dance around a bit, then greet the guest briefly and settle back down. Another dog might throw himself at the door, then body slam the guest and jump all over them, while at the same time barking with excitement. Sure, you can work on this behavior through training, but the truth is, some dogs just start out way more excited than other dogs. This difference in excitement is likely due, at least in part, to differences in the sympathetic nervous system.

Another system that may be influenced by genetics is the other half of the stress response equation—the HPA axis (Maul et al., 2020; Southwick and Charney, 2012). We still need more research on this topic to get a clear picture of what is going on. However, some studies do provide some insight. For example, there are variations in certain genes that influence stress hormone production. These variations are associated with increased resilience and reduced incidence of stress-related mental health disorders after experiencing stress during childhood (Bradley et al., 2008; Laryea et al., 2012; White et al., 2013). Genetic variations that influence various chemical messengers and other factors in the brain are also likely to have impacts on resilience (Maul et al., 2020; Osório et al., 2016). There is even some evidence that there is a genetic influence on the brain's ability to flexibly adapt to the living environment (Ferrari and Villa, 2017)!

In humans, we know that mental health disorders (such as anxiety, depression and PTSD) have a strong genetic component (Duncan et al., 2018; Gottschalk and Domschke, 2017). Estimates vary widely, but they can frequently explain about 30 to 40% of the variability in the occurrence of these disorders (Daskalakis et al., 2018; Gottschalk and Domschke, 2017). That still means that environmental factors account for the rest of the variability. There is still a lot we don't know about the genetics of resilience. However, it is clear that resilience is influenced by genetics to some degree. For example, genetic research on stress resiliency is ongoing. Sometime in the future, researchers hope to have a clear enough picture to identify individuals that may be more vulnerable to stress but we are still a long way away from that at this time.

Gene-by-environment interactions

It's not just genetics that matter. It looks like resilience develops in the same way many other health and behavior conditions develop—as a result of a unique combination of genetics and personal experience. This is called a gene-by-environment interaction. Our genetics provides a base through which our experience is filtered. I think of this as akin to wearing tinted glasses. In high school, I had sunglasses with purple lenses. Wearing them caused the world around me to look just a little different. This is how I view genetics—the way we process and react to our experiences gets filtered through our genetics. It is not *just* genetics or *just* experience that matters. One common analogy is baking. One important aspect of a recipe is the specific ingredients that go into it. Another important aspect is the heat that is used during baking. You wouldn't say that the final product—the bread—was just a result of the ingredients. But it's also not just the heat that matters. It's *how they interact with each other* that's important.

This means it's possible that the same genetic code (**genotype**) may produce different observable characteristics (**phenotypes**), depending on the environment (Ellis and Boyce, 2008). The best way to study this is with identical twins, as they share 100% of their DNA, but not 100% of their experiences. Here is a very simple example. Let's say you have two identical twins. One of them ends up spending a lot of time outside in a sunny climate. The other lives in a cloudier climate and spends most of his time inside. The twin that is outside in a sunny environment will have a darker skin tone than the twin that spends most of their time inside. Same genetic makeup (genotype), but different observable characteristics (phenotype).

Here is another example that is more specific to behavior. Caspi et al. (2003) found that individuals with a history of major stressful life events were more likely to be diagnosed with major depression, but *only* if they had at least one copy of a particular gene variant. Stressful life events did *not* predict depression if the person had two copies of the long version of the gene. If *genetics* were the only thing that mattered, then every person with the short gene variant would show depression. If *experience* were the only thing that mattered, then everyone that experienced a stressful life event would develop depression. Instead, you need to have *both.* To be clear, these two things are not the only things that matter in the development of depression, but when they occurred together, they increased the likelihood that a person would develop depression.

Rats from anxious lines (genes) that were stressed *in utero* became less anxious as adults than those that weren't stressed. But rats from low anxiety lines gene that were stressed *in utero* became *more* stressed as adults. In both cases, the stress changed the brain, but the changes were different in the different genetic strains (Kapoor and Matthews, 2005; Vallée et al., 1997). These results are probably not directly generalizable outside of this study because they relate to very specific, carefully bred, genetic strains of mice—not to *any* animal that has high or low anxiety. However, the point is that the ultimate behavioral outcome depends on both an animal's genetics and experience.

Another example of a gene by environment interaction is gene variants that can be beneficial or detrimental depending on the context. I mentioned before that some animals have a more reactive sympathetic nervous system. If the system is very responsive, that means the animal will have a strong fight-or-flight response to stressors in the environment. Imagine a stray dog that is living on its own. There may be many potential threats, such as cars, other dogs and unfriendly people. If you are living in a threatening environment, a strong fight-or-flight response is probably adaptive—chances are good that many of the sudden sounds, sights or smells the animal encounters in their environment are potentially dangerous. If something is actually dangerous, it warrants a fight-or-flight response, so having a reactive system is a good thing and is likely to aid survival.

Now imagine that a stray dog is caught, brought into a rescue and adopted into a loving family. Now that same individual is living in a relatively safe environment and routinely reacting to sounds, sights and smells with a fight-or-flight response that may not be appropriate. They are spending a lot of time and energy reacting to things that are likely harmless. This creates wear and tear on the body and interferes with the animal's ability to engage in other important behaviors such as feeding, social interaction and rest. As you can imagine, having a more active autonomic nervous system in a safe environment could be a disadvantage. It makes sense—and is biologically adaptive—for an individual to be able to adjust to changes in its environment. Dogs that have trouble adjusting for one reason or another will be less resilient.

Epigenetics

You are no doubt aware that our genes are made up of DNA, or **deoxyribonucleic acid**. Certain sections of DNA provide recipes for proteins. These proteins are responsible for the structure and function of cells. If the sequence of DNA changes, then the gene expression also changes. If you change your favorite brownie recipe, the outcome of the brownies will also change. Depending on the changes you make, the final result could be slightly or dramatically different. For a long time, it was believed that a change in the DNA sequence was the only way to change gene expression. It turns out that's not true. Gene expression can also be changed in other ways. **Epigenetics** is the study of changes in the expression of genes that are not caused by heritable changes to the actual sequence of DNA.

Epigenetic changes can affect health and behavior, but don't change the actual DNA sequence. Epigenetic processes are another way in which the environment and genetics interact to produce behavior. Epigenetic changes can occur after conception (i.e., after the DNA sequence has already been determined) in response to an individual's experience. We know that stress—both acute and chronic—is one factor that can change gene expression (Schiele and Domschke, 2018). We also know that epigenetics plays a role in things like fear acquisition and extinction (Kwapis and Wood, 2014). Because epigenetic changes can be passed to future generations, experiences that parents or grandparents had well before an animal is born can have an impact on the current generation's physiology and behavior. This could, in turn, impact on the current generation's stress resilience.

There are a few ways this could happen, but the best understood mechanism is DNA methylation and that's what we'll focus on here. I mentioned above that certain sections of DNA code for proteins. Sometimes, methyl groups (little clusters of hydrogen and carbon) will attach to a strand of DNA. This is called DNA methylation. The reason this matters to us is that DNA methylation can turn the production of proteins on or off. So, the recipe is still there, but it is no longer being made. Or vice versa. That means that patterns of gene expression can be changed in adults—and in some cases these changes can be passed onto offspring.

There is strong evidence that maternal care causes epigenetic changes that can then be passed on to future generations (Francis et al., 1999; Meaney and Szyf, 2005). It's not only the mother's stress level that matters. Dad's experiences can also cause epigenetic changes. This is true *even when the offspring have never met their father*. One study showed that if male mice were chronically stressed and then bred, their offspring had *decreased* HPA responsiveness (notice this is the opposite of what you see when mom is stressed) (Rodgers et al., 2013). Here's another study that's even more fascinating. Researchers exposed soon-to-be fathers to a certain odor. Then, they associated that odor with something frightening. This caused the fathers to develop a conditioned fear response to the odor. That's not surprising. But they then bred those fathers and found that their children and grandchild showed increased behavioral sensitivity toward that specific odor, but not to other odors (Dias and Ressler, 2014). This means that somehow, the fear that the father learned in association with that specific odor, was passed on to his offspring and his offspring's offspring even though he *never interacted with any of them.* This is shocking! At this point you are probably wondering how this is possible. Great question!

There are several different possibilities (Sandi and Haller, 2015). First, changes in the father's behavior could trigger changes to the mother's behavior that then impact the behavior of the offspring. However, they addressed this possibility by using *in vitro* fertilization—meaning mom and dad never interacted. This suggests that the changes were caused by some kind of change in biology, rather than passed on through social interactions. Researchers believe the changes were caused by epigenetics. In the odor study above, scientists found changes in the methylation of an odor receptor gene—suggesting that epigenetics was playing a role (Dias and Ressler, 2014).

We still have a long way to go to get a full understanding of the influence of genetics on stress resiliency. We know a bit more about the specific aspects of the environment that are important for developing resilience. The rest of this chapter will attempt to lay out the relationship between those factors and the development of stress resiliency in animals.

Personality and coping styles

Another thing that impacts an animal's resiliency is their **personality**. Personality refers to a set of behavioral and physiological responses that are consistent across time and context (Koolhaas and Van Reenen, 2016; Sih, 2011). The way animals respond to stress is often called **coping styles**. Researchers have found that animals have different types of responses to dealing with stress. Animals tend to fall into one of two categories: **bold** or **shy**. There has been relatively little research on the bold/shy personality profile in animals, but the work that has been done suggests that this distinction is relevant to dogs as well.

Just to make sure things are confusing, there are several different names for the same kinds of coping styles. This is partly because there is some disagreement over the best term to use and partly due to differences in terminology between different (but closely related) fields. So, you might also see bold animals referred to as **active** or **proactive** or see shy individuals referred to as **passive** or **reactive**. For our purposes, these terms are essentially interchangeable. I chose to use bold and shy because they are less likely to cause confusion with other terminology already being used in the dog training field.

Animals, including dogs, with a bold coping style have a bolder personality. That means, for example, that they may be quicker to approach a novel object. They are also quicker to display aggressive behavior (Huntingford, 1982; Bell and Sih, 2007). This bold behavior is linked to increased risk-taking and may make bold animals more likely to be injured or fall victim to predation (Bell and Sih, 2007; Dingemans et al., 2007). Shy animals, on the other hand, are more cautious and tend to avoid risk. This means they are at lower risk for injury and predation so likely to live longer (at least in the wild). They show passive coping and have low levels of aggression (Koolhaas and Van Reenen, 2016).

What exactly does this *look* like? Studies in rodents often focus on two different aspects of behavior: attack latency and defensive burying. **Attack latency** is a measure of how long it takes the resident rat to attack an 'intruder' rat when the intruder enters the resident's home cage. Bold rats show shorter attack latencies—that is, they are quicker to attack the other rat.

Another way of testing the difference between bold and shy rats is the defensive burying test. In this test, a scary object (often a prod that administers a mild electric shock) is placed in the rodent's cage. If they touch the object during the course of investigation, they receive a mild shock. The rats then tend to react in one of two different ways. They will either bury the prod (defensive burying) or avoid the prod by freezing. Can you guess which behavior is demonstrated by bold individuals and which by shy? The bold individuals bury the prod, while the shy individuals freeze. Hence, the bold animals have a more active, or proactive, response and the shy animals have a more reactive, or passive, response.

Bold individuals also tend to show a characteristic physiological response to stress. They show low **HPA reactivity**, but high **sympathetic arousal** (Fokkema et al., 1995). This means that when faced with a stressor, bold animals tend to release lower levels of stress hormones (low HPA reactivity) and show more arousal. Bold animals also cope more effectively with stress than shy animals (Wood and Bhatnagar, 2015).

Like bold individuals, shy animals show a characteristic physiological reaction to stress, but in the opposite direction. Shy animals release high levels of stress hormones (high HPA reactivity) and show relatively low levels of sympathetic arousal in response to stress (Korte et al., 1992; Fokkema et al., 1988). The passive coping favored by shy individuals is associated with higher levels of distress and depressive symptoms in humans (Wood and Bhatnagar, 2015) as well as decreased immune function (Wood et al., 2015).

You may have heard the terminology of stressing up and stressing down when we talk about our dogs. I think this is likely an illustration of the two different coping styles. Some dogs become more active when stressed, and may progress to jumping, mouthing, barking and potentially aggressive behavior. I suspect these dogs fit the bold profile. On the other hand, some dogs stress down and show avoidance and freezing (shutting down) behavior. These dogs are likely on the shy end of the spectrum. To my knowledge no one has tested this yet, but my guess is that if you took the bold (or stress up) dogs, you would find that they show strong sympathetic arousal and relatively low levels of stress. In contrast, I suspect that the shy (or stress down dogs) show the opposite pattern—lower sympathetic arousal, but a greater release of stress hormones. Of course, these are just educated guesses, so please don't make any important decisions based on this information!

There has been very little research on coping styles specific to dogs, but the studies that have been done show evidence for a bold/shy profile in dogs. Horváth et al. (2007) used statistical analysis to identify three different coping styles in a group of police dogs. They labeled the three groups fearfulness, aggressiveness and ambivalence. The dogs that showed higher levels of aggression, shorter attack latency and more activity, also showed no change in stress hormones after a stressor. Wood et al. (2014) found dogs that retreated from the sound of another dog growling showed much stronger cortisol responses than those that approached the growl. The results of both studies are consistent with the characterization that bold animals tend to have decreased stress reactivity, whereas shy animals tend to show higher stress reactivity.

Corsetti and colleagues (2018) studied the impact of coping style on vulnerability to disease in animal shelters. It should be unsurprising by now—given the relationship between stress and health—to learn that coping style also has implications for health and the immune system. The researchers found that dogs with a bold personality style were healthier after 30 days of observation than dogs with a shy personality. This is consistent with other research that shows a relationship between stress and immune function (Glaser and Kiecolt-Glaser, 2005). Still, it is very important to remember that the Corsetti study is only one study, and we can never draw strong conclusions from a single study. I only bring it up here because it's the only study I am aware of that has been done specifically on coping styles in dogs.

The bold/shy dimension is probably not the only aspect of personality. Koolhaas and Van Reenen (2016) argue that coping style explains how an animal responds to stress. That is, it is *qualitative*. However, there is another factor that is also very important and that is how *intensely* an animal responds to stress. They refer to this second, quantitative, measure as **emotionality**. Emotionality is very poorly defined in the literature, but in this context, it means animals that respond more intensely to stimuli are more emotional. For example, a dog may be high or low in fear. A dog with a shy coping style and low fear may not even register a particular event as stressful and therefore have no response to it at all. But a dog with a bold coping style and high fear may react very strongly to a stressor. In this case, the bold dog may show more of an approach style when feeling fearful, rather than the avoid strategy you might see in a shy animal. A bold/fearful animal would be showing a stress reaction much more often than a shy/non-fearful animal because of the difference in emotionality.

Coping style and emotionality seem to be key to resilience. But what influences the development of these traits? How exactly these coping styles develop is still unclear, but there is a lot we do know.

Early life experiences

As we've already discussed in this book, early experience plays an important role in shaping future behavior. Here, we will cover this topic in more detail as it relates to the development of resiliency. Again, chronic stress has very detrimental effects, particularly during development. The longer the stress continues, the more negative the impact (Eyck et al., 2019). This is true in a wide range of species from mammals to amphibians to spiders (reviewed in Eyck, 2019). It appears that these impacts can be irreversible (Langenhof and Komdeur, 2018). As we have already discussed, adversity experienced during early development is associated with increased stress reactivity and causes dramatic changes to the brain, particularly in the fear circuit. However, remember that our understanding of the development of stress resiliency is only just beginning—early experience only accounts for a very small percentage of the variability in how an animal responds to stress (Eyck et al., 2019). This tells us that there are other factors that are also important, but that we probably haven't clearly identified all of them yet. One of those factors may be the importance of experiencing *some*, but not too much, stress during development.

Moderate non-toxic stress in juveniles

There is evidence from a few different studies that animals that experience *moderate* levels of stress during development— rather than mild or severe stress— actually show increased stress resiliency. This is sometimes referred to as a stress inoculation effect (Lyons et al., 2009). The first evidence of this was found in rats. Rats that are removed from their cage and gently touched by the experimenter for a few seconds in the first few weeks of life, show reduced anxiety and fearfulness, and improved stress coping later in life (reviewed in Fernández-Teruel et al., 2002).

It is now clear that females and males respond differently to developmental stress, but the research on exactly *how* they respond differently is still unclear (see Bath, 2020 for review). For example, a few studies have found that handling seems to have a protective effect on future exposure to stress in males, but may make females more vulnerable (Papaioannou et al., 2002; Park et al., 2003). The details of how early exposure to stress varies with sex likely depends on a number of different factors. Possible factors include age at stress exposure, type and duration of stress and genetics. We also do not have a clear understanding of the role that surgical sterilization may have on an animal's response to stress. We know that hormones can have a dramatic influence on behavior. Further, sex differences in the impact of early stress in rodents are likely driven, at least in part, by differences in sex hormones. Therefore, it seems likely that surgical sterilization does impact the development of resiliency, but it is difficult to say for sure until we have quite a bit more research.

In addition, some researchers have suggested that it's not the handling itself that is impacting behavior. Reunification with mom after separation prompts *increased maternal care*. It may be the increased maternal care that matters, rather than the handling itself (Parker and Maestripieri, 2011). Indeed, similar outcomes are seen in offspring who are not handled, but who experience high quality maternal care (Liu et al., 1997).

There is some evidence that mild to moderate levels of stress impact stress hormone production. Rodents and primates that are repeatedly exposed to novelty at a young age or experience *brief* separations from mom show less HPA reactivity as adolescents and adults. However, we do not have a lot of information yet about the effect on actual behavior (Romeo, 2015).

Predictable, intermittent stress in rats during adolescence can improve stress coping in adults. Rats subjected to five minutes per day of predictable stress had less anxiety and depression-like behavior as young adults (Suo et al., 2013). In this case, predictable stress meant that the rats were exposed to the same type of stressor (restraint) for the same amount of time (5 minutes) at the same time each day.

Humans have shown increased stress resilience if they were exposed to moderate levels of stress as a child (Khoshaba and Maddi, 1999; Gunnar et al., 2009). Similar results have also been found in squirrel monkeys. Young squirrel monkeys were separated from their mothers for an hour a day. The separated young showed less anxiety and decreased stress hormones production in a new environment during late childhood compared to young that had not been separated (Parker et al., 2004). Another study showed that separated young demonstrated more cognitive control of behavior and improved behavioral flexibility and impulse control (Parker et al., 2005) than those not separated. Separated monkeys have also shown increased curiosity and exploratory behavior when tested during adolescence (Parker et al., 2007). Similar results have been seen in rats (Kendig et al., 2011).

So, there is some evidence that suggests that **moderate stress** early in life can improve stress resiliency later in life. However, what exactly is moderate stress? How do we define this? Researchers have suggested that is has several features. First, it appears that the stressful experiences need to be brief and intermittent. Prolonged periods of stress are still damaging.

In addition, moderate stress, to be beneficial, needs to be challenging, but not overwhelming. Put another way, an animal needs to be able to *effectively cope with the stressor in the moment.* This is a critically important point! In effect, we are talking about good and tolerable stress, *not* toxic stress. To be on the safe side, we should aim for just good stress. Remember, tolerable stress is still distressing and it's going to be very difficult to determine ahead of time when tolerable crosses the line into toxic. Therefore, we don't want to intentionally put dogs into distressing situations. Instead, we aim for good stress which is challenging, but not distressing. Tolerable stress is still likely to happen on its own and that's okay—we can't control everything! But I cannot, in good conscience, recommend intentionally distressing puppies in an attempt to improve their resiliency. There is simply too much we don't know about the details of this process to do so safely.

Researchers also suggest that stress needs to mimic naturally occurring conditions. The process of weaning is most likely distressing for puppies. However, it is something that occurs naturally. Therefore, the stress of weaning may actually help the puppies learn to cope with other stressors later in life. This means it probably falls into the category of tolerable stress. However, if puppies are weaned too early, the weaning process doesn't mimic natural conditions. Early weaning seems to cause toxic stress in many cases and can have long-lasting detrimental effects, as discussed earlier in the book.

The current thinking across disciplines is that early experiences prepare animals for later environments. This makes sense because in many cases the developmental environment is a good predictor of the adult environment. An animal born into a challenging environment would want to be prepared to continue to survive in a challenging environment. On the other hand, an animal born into a relatively safe, less challenging environment, should be optimized for thriving in a safe environment. It would be beneficial for animals to be flexible during development in this way because some time periods are much more challenging and difficult than others. One generation might be born during a drought, for example, when food is scarce. But, 20 years later, food could be abundant. These two generations will face different challenges and may benefit from different sets of skills. If a species has a built-in mechanism for preparing their offspring for success in different environments (harsh or abundant), they will have an advantage over species that are less flexible.

Several researchers have proposed that issues arise when there is a mismatch between the early rearing environment and the later environment as the animal is prepared for one environment but ends up living in another environment (Nederhof and Schmidt, 2012). For example, a dog raised in a high stress environment is going to 'expect' to live in a high stress environment as an adult. When they are instead in a stable, safe environment, there is a mismatch. They developed to cope with a dangerous environment but the skills that would have served them well there (such as increased fear and hypervigilance) often create problems in a typical family home.

This is a good time to remind you that this area of research is very young and incomplete. That means that there is likely more going on here that we don't understand yet, so we need to be cautious with our interpretation and application of this information. It's also important to understand that early experiences only account for a small portion of the variation in stress resilience so there are still large pieces of the puzzle that are completely missing at this time.

The opportunity for the dog to exert control

Another factor that plays an important role in an animal's ability to cope with stress is the ability to exert some degree of control. Lack of control has been linked to increased anxiety- and depression-like behavior. Seminal work was done on the impact of control on behavior in dogs in the 1960s. This research was done several decades ago and is difficult to read about, but it has produced important results that have greatly informed how we view behavior today, so I will discuss it here.

Students in Richard Solomon's lab at the University of Pennsylvania discovered that if dogs were subjected to inescapable shock they then would not attempt to escape later even if given the opportunity (Maier and Seligman, 2016). Steven Maier and Martin Seligman took these findings and explored them further (Overmier and Seligman, 1967; Maier and Seligman, 2016). They came up with the following model. First, dogs learn they have no control and that escape is not an option in one context. Then, they generalize that to other contexts. The dog believes that their behavior has no effect on their environment in *general*. To use the technical term, they learn their behavior is **non-contingent**. As a result, they stop trying to escape their circumstances, or attempting to manipulate their environment to their benefit. This is called **learned helplessness**. Research in humans has shown that learned helplessness is associated with depression (Klein et al., 1976).

More recent work has taken the concept of control one step further. Moscarello and Hartley (2017) have proposed a unifying model of how control molds an animal's perspective of the world in ways that can have a profound influence on behavior. They suggest that animals make decisions about how to behave in an environment based on their beliefs about their level of control, or agency. If an animal has learned in the past that their behavior does not impact or change the world around them (that is, their behavior is non-contingent), they are going to be very unlikely to try to change that world. On the other hand, if they have learned that their behavior has an impact on the world around them (their behavior is **contingent**), then they will be much more likely to try to influence the outcome.

Animals with a history of control engage in more exploratory and flexible behavior. They show more goal-directed behavior (as opposed to habitual behavior). This behavioral profile is referred to as **proactive**. Moscarello and Hartley propose that proactive animals interact with their environment from the perspective of "what can I do in this environment?" (2017). This allows them to take advantage of the opportunities in a particular environment.

Why not do this all the time? First of all, exploration and interaction with the environment also put animals at increased risk for injury, predation or attack. Secondly, proactive behavior uses more resources and there is a disadvantage to spending those resources unless you actually have the ability to influence your environment.

When an animal does not have a lot of control—or they think they do not—they are more **reactive**. In this case, Moscarello and Hartley suggest that animals view their world from the perspective of "what can this environment do to me?" (2017). These animals display rapid, innate, defensive responses to perceived threats or rewards in the environment. There is much less cognitive processing involved. Moscarello and Hartley call this behavioral profile reactive. (Note that this is a different definition of reactive and does not refer directly to barking and lunging on leash.) Being reactive makes sense in an environment when you have little or no control because reactivity is quick and uses relatively few resources.

Moscarello and Hartley go on to argue that both proactive and reactive profiles can be beneficial in certain environments. However, they are both problematic if there is a mismatch between the animal's estimate of agency (control) and their actual level of control. Reactive behavior, on the other hand, becomes a problem in situations where the animal actually does have control. In this case, that animal loses out on opportunities for exploration and is not able to take full advantage of their environment. Reactive behavior also interferes with other important behaviors such as rest, eating, and social interaction.

Is it a lack of control or coping style?
All this may sound very similar to the discussion on coping style and early environmental experiences. It's true—these concepts are very closely related and there is quite a bit of overlap among them. There are a few distinctions, though:

Coping styles are consistent across the lifetime and in different contexts. We have limited ability to change an animal's coping style.

Early experience refers to experiences during development *(in utero through adolescence)*. These experiences likely influence coping style. We can influence this during development but can do nothing to change it in adults.

The **estimates of agency model** developed by Moscarello and Hartley states that the collective experiences of an animal's ability to influence their environment impacts how they view the world. In my opinion, we have a great deal of power to change this by giving our dogs more agency.

Intensity and predictability of stressors

One significant factor relating to resiliency is the intensity and predictability of stressors the dog experiences. To some extent this is a matter of luck, although good management on the part of the owner can impact this. Obviously, stressors that are more intense have a greater impact. A Category Five hurricane is much more stressful than a brief thunderstorm. In addition, predictable stressors tend to be less distressing than unpredictable stressors. Let's look at an example. Imagine living with an aggressive dog. In the beginning, there were a couple bites, and one even required stitches. However, over time, you have learned that your dog only shows aggression in very predictable circumstances—when you try to take a stolen item or bone from her. You've even learned to read her body language and predict when she is preparing to bite. As a result, you have learned to manage the aggression; there has not been a bite in a long time and it is no longer as upsetting as it used to be.

Contrast this experience with a different dog. This dog has bitten, but never hard enough to require stitches. In this case, you are not able to find any rhyme or reason for the bites. They appear to happen out of the blue. Sometimes she reacts to being handled or sitting next to her on the couch, other times she seems happy to have the company. In addition, you have not been able to identify any warning signals. Sometimes long periods of time will go by with no signs of aggression, then it will suddenly appear again.

Which dog do you think would be more stressful to live with? Probably the unpredictable dog, even though her bites haven't been as severe. Researchers have speculated that when stressors are unpredictable, it may make it difficult for the animal to identify specific predictors of an aversive stimulus. Because the animal never knows when or if something unpleasant is going to happen, they develop a state of generalized anxiety. Unpredictable stressors may also make it more difficult to cope effectively. Finally, they can also reduce the perception of control.

One of the primary rodent models for studying depression is the chronic unpredictable mild stress model. In this model, animals are exposed to unpredictable "micro-stressors" over an extended period of time. Example of stressors include being placed in an empty cage and sometimes keeping the lights on overnight. So, they are not experiencing major stress and they are not experiencing it all the time. But it is chronic, and it is unpredictable. This procedure causes decreased interest in rewards and learned helplessness (Willner et al., 1987; Hu et al., 2017). Other changes include cognitive impairments, decreased activity, disruptions to sleep, weight loss, decreased aggression and sexual behavior, and often (but not always) increased anxiety (Willner, 2005; Luo et al., 2016).

Unpredictable maternal care is also associated with a wide range of cognitive and emotional problems including impaired learning and memory and increased fear and anxiety (see Molet et al., 2014 for review).

Flexibility

Finally, you may have noticed that a recurring theme is the ability for an animal to be flexible. One key factor in successful stress coping is flexibility (McEwan et al., 2015). The animal needs to be able to adapt to its environment so that they can adjust to change and maintain allostasis. ('Adapt' in this case refers to individual adaptation, not adaptation from an evolutionary perspective. That's important too, but that occurs at a species level, rather than an individual level.) Animals that experience high levels of stress during development seem to be less able to respond flexibly. In fact, stress causes the brain itself to become less flexible, or less "plastic" (McEwen et al., 2015).

Chapter summary

Some animals are more resilient and can cope better with stress than others. Figuring out what drives these differences is the holy grail of dog training and behavior work. We can't prevent all bad things from happening, but if we can learn how to help our dogs (and ourselves!)

overcome the adversity in their lives, we could make a world-shifting change in their quality of life. We still do not have the full picture of why some animals are more resilient than others. You can think of our current understanding as akin to looking through a microscope with a dirty lens. Some parts of the lens are completely blacked out, others are cloudy, but we can see part of the picture and there are a few areas that are quite clear. The next several decades show great promise in bringing new breakthroughs in the prevention and treatment of stress-related disorders—in both humans and dogs!

How do I interpret the current evidence? I interpret it as support for what so many of us are already doing. As owners and dog professionals, it is our job to create a world that empowers our dogs to thrive. If we are to succeed at this, we must first understand the impacts of stress and the factors that influence the development of resilience. The next step is figuring out *how we can improve* a dog's ability to cope with stress in the moment. That is what we will cover in the next chapter.

Chapter 6
Helping Your Dog to Avoid or Cope with Stress

Hopefully by now you have been fully convinced that toxic stress is a problem and that we need to do our best to avoid or minimize it in our animals. However, I am not one to leave people with bad news and nothing to do about it! The previous chapter talked about how resiliency develops. But what happens when your dog needs help to avoid or reduce stress? This chapter will discuss what we can do to help our animals cope better with stress that they are currently experiencing. There are several things to help your dog avoid or cope with stress:

- Reduce stress during development
- Provide predictability and control
- Provide social support
- Enrichment
- Exercise
- Use proper training methods
- Skilled application of behavior modification to extinguish fear and anxiety

What about medications?
Medications can also help improve an animal's ability to cope with stress. Remember that stress can cause changes to the brain and the stress response system. Medication can help address those changes. However, because this book is focused on behavioral interventions

it does not include a detailed discussion of medication. Medications are not called for in all cases, especially for dogs that aren't showing major behavior issues or signs of toxic stress. However, if your dog is showing aggression or high levels of fear or anxiety or is not responding to the environmental and behavioral interventions mentioned here, I recommend consulting with your veterinarian or a veterinary behaviorist to investigate possible medical issues and discuss the possibility of psychotropic medication and behavioral modification options.

Reduce stress during development

As I outlined in Chapter 3, maternal care is an important component of development. Poor maternal care has been associated with increased anxiety- and depression-like behaviors later in life. Care should be made to reduce stress in pregnant and nursing mothers. Mothers should be allowed to leave the whelping box of their own accord but forced absences should be avoided whenever possible.

Of course, avoiding separation is not always realistic for a variety of reasons. In these cases, there may be a few things we can do to help. In rodents, changes due to a single, day-long separation can be prevented by simulating maternal care. This was done by feeding the pups and brushing the genital region with a moist brush to simulate the mother grooming the pups (Van Oers et al., 1998; Van Oers et al., 2001). A similar procedure could be done with puppies.

For more chronic separation, researchers have found that placing pups in same age foster litters during maternal separation abolished the effects of maternal separation (Huot et al., 2004). This suggests that it's not just the presence of the biological mother that is important, but also the care itself. Indeed, quality of care can impact anxiety- and depression-like behavior later in life (Cui et al., 2006; Dalle Molle et al,. 2012). Treating the adult offspring with antidepressants also helped reduce the impacts of maternal separation, but only as long as the medication was actively being administered (Huot et al., 2001; Plotsky et al., 1997). Once the medication ended, the behavioral effects returned.

Whenever possible, puppies separated from their mothers for an extended period (including in cases where the mother is completely absent), should be placed with a foster mother, ideally with puppies of the same age as the orphan litter. When this is not possible, it's important that potential adopters be educated that their puppy is likely going to be more vulnerable to stress. The point of this is not to scare off potential adopters. Rather, they can be taught how to counteract these tendencies as much as possible. These adopters are going to need to have a higher level of education and commitment and are going to need more support than those adopting puppies that have not experienced high levels of stress during development. This applies to those adopting puppies coming from high stress environments, not just those who have been separated too early from mom.

If you are getting a dog from a breeder, look for a breeder who breeds dogs with a balanced temperament. You probably should avoid a dog that is on one end of the extreme in terms of boldness or shyness. Also look for dogs who don't have particularly intense responses to stimuli in their environment, or for puppies who seem very social. This is easier said than done, of course! However, the more you can learn about the breeder, the breeder's line of dogs, the puppies in the litter and the breeding practices, the better. Meeting other dogs in the line is a great opportunity to get a feel for the genetics of that line of dogs.

Socialize your puppies, but make sure you do it in way that it is not distressing to them. Never force them to approach or remain in a situation that makes them afraid or uncomfortable. Give them control over the situation and give them the opportunity to opt out whenever they want. Watch the puppy's body language to determine the type of stress they are experiencing. Signs of distress include low body posture, lowered ears and head or a low or tucked tail, avoiding eye contact, weight centered over the rear legs, lip licking, yawning, closed mouth and struggling or attempting to escape. If you are not sure they are enjoying themselves, leave the situation and bring them somewhere they feel more comfortable.

In addition, try to teach puppies that their behavior matters. Giving them the opportunity to opt out of situations they don't enjoy is one way to do this. Positive reinforcement training is another great option. Later in this chapter, I will discuss several strategies you can use to increase control in dogs and these can be applied to puppies as well as adults.

There is one thing I recommend changing that involves adolescent dogs. I think we need to pay more attention to socialization and emotional health with them. We have ample evidence that an animal's experiences during adolescence can impact their behavior later in life. I believe it is important to continue socialization past 12 weeks all the way through adolescence (at least until one and a half to two years). This is especially true when it comes to opportunities to play with other, age-matched (and friendly) dogs.

Research presented earlier in the book suggests that increasing our attention to social interaction and play during adolescence could have a profound impact on the well-being of our dogs. Many shelters have already caught onto the benefits of dog-dog social interaction and are making a point to (carefully) provide dogs with more opportunities for social interaction and play. Pet dog trainers and day care centers are also in a great position to help address this issue. Programs that 1) incorporate education about appropriate play and its benefits, and 2) provide increased opportunities for safe and appropriate play for adolescents could have a dramatic impact on the social well-being of dogs. This, in turn, may help them cope better with stress and reduce the likelihood of behavior issues.

It is also key for us to be mindful of a dog's stress level during their "teenage" years and make sure that we do everything we can to avoid putting them into overwhelming situations. Letting a dog approach, interact, and retreat at their own pace is critically important! I suspect that allowing puppies and adolescents to observe, approach and interact with their environment is a crucial aspect of socialization. This means that when a young dog stops to look at something we should allow her to look instead of hurrying her along. When safe and appropriate, we should also allow young dogs to investigate novel objects. This gives them the opportunity to learn that the objects are not a threat and teaches them an appropriate method for coping with stress and uncertainty.

Provide predictability and control

Both predictability and control can affect how a dog experiences stress. Remember that it's not the stressor itself that matters, but rather the dog's perception of that stressor. Lack of predictability and control tend to cause stressors to be perceived as more aversive. In this chapter we will look at how you, as the dog's owner, can build more predictability and control in your dog's life.

Predictability

As the owner (or a trainer working with an owner), you can take steps to help your dog identify predictive cues to what otherwise could lead to what the dog perceives as unpredictable stress. Many dogs cannot anticipate when something unpleasant is going to happen. This may lead to *generalized* fear and anxiety in certain contexts rather than becoming afraid of a specific stimulus (Baas et al., 2008; Grupe and Nitschke, 2013). If unpredictable stress occurs in multiple contexts, then the animal could develop a generalized anxiety to all (or many) contexts, particularly unfamiliar ones.

Therefore, increasing predictability is likely to improve a dog's ability to cope with stress. When I think of predictability, I often think of the daily routine. Imagine an anxious dog that lives in a very chaotic household where the schedule varies widely. This could be contributing to his stress. Putting him on a more predictable schedule may help. However, it is not just the day-to-day routine that matters. Likely the most important thing is the ability to predict the stressors themselves. This may explain why dogs with separation distress may be more likely to display separation-related behavior when there is a change in the normal routine.

An environment where the reaction to the dog's behavior is very unpredictable is likely very stressful for the dog. For example, if the dog is sometimes yelled at for jumping on people and sometimes welcomed, they never have an opportunity to learn the rules—and therefore will have difficulty learning how to avoid punishment. Imagine how stressful it would be to never know when you might get yelled at, or how to avoid it! That effect is magnified if it happens across many different contexts in everyday life. Pulling is okay today but wasn't yesterday. It's okay if you bark at that person, but not this person. And so on. I am sure that this happens a lot in pet homes. This is one reason why consistency is so important! Make sure that everyone who interacts with the dog knowns what is expected of the dog. It can also be very helpful to spend some time thinking about your expectations for the dog—to make sure that you are not changing the rules from one day to the next!

Neither of my dogs liked having their nails clipped so I went through an extensive process of getting them comfortable with the procedure. My normal routine when dremeling my dogs' nails is to get a cup of food and walk upstairs to our guest room. I'll then sit on the bed and go through the same routine each time, starting with the same toe of the same foot and going in the same order. When I walk upstairs to get started, my dogs jump off the couch, charge upstairs, jump on the bed and immediately get in position for grooming. When I'm really on point, I will even work with them at the same time each day. However, if I try to dremel their nails in my living room, they struggle, and try to pull their paw out of my hand. It's a very unpleasant experience for both of us.

Why the difference? For one, I think there is an issue with context and lack of generalization since we have done the bulk of the work in the guest room. However, I suspect that predictability plays a role as well. Because I go through the same process every time, they know exactly what is going to happen, and when. The living room is less predictable and, therefore, more stressful. As a result, I no longer do their nails anywhere but in the guest room.

Control

Control is another major factor in terms of determining how well an animal can cope with stress. Lack of control can lead to a long list of negative outcomes. It is associated with decreased learning, exploration and social behavior, and increased fear of novelty, gastrointestinal issues, anxiety- and depression-like behavior and fear learning (see Maier and Watkins, 2005, for review). We talked about control in Chapter 5 as well, in relation to the development of learned helplessness and resiliency. That discussion involved how prior experience with control can impact an animal's ability to cope with stress. Now we're talking about what you can do with the dog you have in front of you, regardless of their prior experience with control.

If your dog is put into a position where she cannot avoid a situation that causes her distress, research suggests that she will tend to show increased defensive behavior (e.g., freezing), decreased social exploration, and decreased instrumental learning (Barratta et al., 2007; Christianson et al., 2008; Lucas et al., 2014). On the other hand, if animals learn that they have the power to stop an unpleasant experience, they will show decreased freezing and increased exploration and learning and improved resilience to uncontrollable stress later in life (Lucas et al., 2014; Maier, 2015).

Control over something aversive can increase learning and decrease fear. However, it turns out that you get *the same effect* from control over access to reinforcements. That is, *control over rewards* appears to be just as effective at improving resilience as providing control over punishers!

Studies done on rats by Goodkin (1976) showed interesting results relating to a rat's ability to learn to avoid aversives. Getting access to free (non-contingent) rewards may actually impair an animal's ability to learn. There are aspects of this study that are upsetting, but I think the information is so valuable that I am reporting it here. In one study, two groups of rats were trained to perform a behavior for food (using either a nose push or pull chain). Another group was trained to pull a chain to avoid a shock. A fourth and fifth group received either non-contingent food or shock. That is, they received the food/ shock regardless of their behavior and had no ability to stop or avoid the food or shock. The sixth and final group (the control group) received no manipulation at all.

All six groups were tested on their ability to learn to perform a nose push to avoid a shock. Which rats do you think learned to push the button most quickly? You might guess it was the rats that learned to pull the chain to avoid a shock. Afterall, the chain pullers had already learned that their behavior could stop the shock. Or maybe you think the rats that learned to nose push for food would learn the fastest. The nose pushers had already learned that pushing the button with their nose benefited them. This is partially correct, but it is not the whole story.

As you can see in the chart below, what happened was that the three groups with previous operant learning experience (nose push for food, pull chain for food and pull chain to avoid shock) learned the new task the fastest—and they all learned it at the same rate. The control group also learned, but more slowly. What about the two groups whose behavior was non-contingent? They *didn't learn the procedure at all,* even after five days of training! The lack of control over avoiding something unpleasant (the shock) or receiving something good (the food) impaired future learning. This means that learning they have control over things will also likely help a dog learn to avoid bad things. In other words, teaching dogs that their behavior matters through positive reinforcement training should improve their stress coping skills and increase their resiliency.

Group number	Condition	Learn nose push to avoid aversive (shock)
1	Nose push = food reward	Learned quickly
2	Pull chain = food reward	Learned quickly
3	Pull chain = avoid shock	Learned quickly
4	Uncontrollable (non-contingent) food	Couldn't learn
5	Uncontrollable (non-contingent) shock	Couldn't learn
6	No manipulation (control group)	Learned slowly

Another study found that rats raised with control over their environment showed fewer signs of reactive and defensive behavior than rats raised without control. In this case, they had control over their lighting conditions and their access to food and water (Joffe et al., 1973). The other rats in the study received the same amount of light, food, and water, but did not control their access to those items. The 'no control' rats showed more fear and anxiety-related behavior, such as clinging to walls and avoiding open areas. Similar results have been shown in young rhesus monkeys. Monkeys with control over food, water and treats during development showed more exploratory behavior and lower levels of fear (Mineka et al., 1986).

This phenomenon is called **generalizing across valence**—the same effect occurs when the animal has control over a desirable outcome as it does for an undesirable outcome. There is no need to use punishment to help dogs cope better with stress, because control over reinforcement will do the trick as well! This may remind you of the Moscarello and Hartley model that we discussed in Chapter 5 and indeed, both concepts are very closely related!

I have been asked if the research on controllable shock provides support for training with aversives. I don't think so. If someone tries to use the evidence on controllable shock to make an argument for using aversives in dogs, they are missing two key points. Yes, it's true that controllable shock is better than uncontrollable shock. But the use of aversives still causes distress. Research on using aversives with dogs indicates that they decrease welfare, but there is little evidence that they improve the outcome of training (see the section on training methods later in this chapter for a detailed review). Furthermore, control of rewards is just as effective as control over aversives, so there really is no argument for using aversives. You can get the same results with rewards, without causing pain or distress. Therefore, rather than supporting aversives, this research strengthens the argument for avoiding aversives and using positive reinforcement instead.

This is huge and has so many implications! It is also incredibly good news! It means we can help our dogs cope with stress by increasing the amount of control they have in their lives. This means that stress for these animals is more likely to be tolerable (or even good). There are many ways we can increase control in our dog's lives.

Practical techniques for giving your dog more control

Ask your dog for consent. This can be something as simple as respecting your dog's choice not to cuddle with you. It can also include more formal consent training in the form of cooperative care. For example, teaching a dog to do a chin rest while cleaning his ears. If the dog chooses to maintain the chin rest, they are offering consent, but if they choose to remove their chin, the ear cleaning stops. The details of this training are covered elsewhere and are beyond the scope of this book, but this is one example of how to increase control in your dog's life.

Other ways of increasing control are letting your dog choose what direction to go on a walk and offering them a choice between different types of toys before play. With my dog Finn, I will place three toys in a row and ask him to pick one. He pounces on one toy and runs around with it and that's the one we play with. He absolutely loves this game, and it has made play sessions much more enjoyable for both of us!

I have also taught my dogs the phrase, "In or out? One...two... three." I use this when I want them to choose whether they want to be inside or not. After I count to three, I close the door. If they haven't come in or gone out yet, they are stuck there for a little while until I come to offer them the choice again. All my dogs seem to have learned the meaning of the phrase and will often make a decision at the last minute and dash through the doorway or turn away and choose to stay where they are.

Learn how to be an expert at reading your dog's body language and give them the opportunity to opt out of experiences that are not enjoyable to them. Of course, there are certain situations, like veterinary care, where we may not be able to give our animals a choice. This is where cooperative care training can really come into play. Programs like Fear Free and Fenzi's TEAM titling program in cooperative care are excellent ways to help increase control for the animal even in situations where the care itself is not optional.

Control goes beyond simply letting the dog choose to engage or not engage in certain experiences. Remember that part of control is simply learning that their behavior has an impact on the world around them—that their behavior is contingent. A study by McGowan et al. (2014) taught a group of kenneled beagles to operate a device for reinforcement. Once they learned how to use the device, the dogs were divided into two groups. In Group One, operating the device correctly caused the door to open, giving them access to a reinforcer. In Group Two, the device did not cause the door to open. Instead, the door for the Group Two dogs would only open after the same amount of time as it took the dog in Group One to succeed.

Let's say that dog #1 in Group One took 24 seconds to use the device successfully and open the door to their pen. In that case, the door for dog #1 in Group Two would also open after 24 seconds, *regardless of whether or not that dog had engaged with the device.* This method means that both dogs are in the pen for the same amount of time, but one dog's behavior is contingent (he or she has control) and one dog's behavior is non-contingent (no control). Dogs in Group One were very excited to enter the testing area, but dogs in Group Two were reluctant to enter after the first few sessions. Not having control is very aversive!

This means teaching your dog that what they do matters is important to reducing stress. Learning how to recognize and respond appropriately to your dog's body language is a huge part of this picture. It allows a dog to learn that the signals they give can influence the behavior of the people around them. Imagine if you were living in a world where people sometimes did scary, painful or uncomfortable things to you despite you repeatedly telling them to stop. In fact, your behavior and pleas to stop weren't acknowledged at all. You can imagine that this would be extremely stressful. Some of our dogs are living that scenario every day of their lives!

The impact of increasing control may be most obvious with fearful dogs. One of my favorite techniques to use with fearful dogs is shaping targeting behaviors. I usually start with something flat and non-threatening, like a carpet square or a notebook. If the dog looks at the target, I toss a treat behind the dog. This avoids placing any pressure on him to approach the item. Once the dog is consistently looking at the target, I will reward him for any forward movement toward the target. Eventually he is reinforced for touching the target.

It's extremely important when using this method that dogs have full control. That means they should not be forced or pressured to approach the object in any way. Over time, I have learned that even things like verbal encouragement, luring or placing a trail of treats may be too much pressure for the dog. Instead, I give them full control and let them continue at their own pace. I have them off leash as long as it's safe to do so. If they are on leash, I make sure to keep the leash loose and quiet. If they choose to leave, that's completely acceptable. (Though, if this happens repeatedly, there is probably something about the situation that is too scary and needs to be adjusted).

I like this method for a couple of reasons. First, the dog has the option to opt out at any time. That is, they have some control over the situation. Second, the dog learns that her behavior matters. According to the research above, if we do this enough, it may help the dog cope with stress in the future. The process is also pairing something unfamiliar (the target) with something good (the food), which can help teach the dog that unfamiliar objects predict good things. It is not only helpful for working with fearful dogs, of course. It's a great way of preventing issues by teaching resilience from the very beginning!

What about free-feeding?

The research on control calls into question the idea of free-feeding which indeed gives the dog the choice of when to eat. Should we free feed our dogs? Does giving dogs access to food at all times, regardless of their behaviors, increase or decrease their quality of life? Does it impact their ability to learn to be proactive in their environment? My honest answer to these questions is that I don't know. We need more dog-specific and context-specific research to be sure, but what we do know certainly suggests that free-feeding may be problematic. In fact, even feeding at scheduled times may be problematic, because the dog still has no control over the arrival of food.

Perhaps it's time for us to completely rethink how to deliver food to our dogs. Part of my goal in writing this book is to release this information into this world and let dog trainers do what they do best—come up with innovative solutions for changing behavior and improving well-being in our dogs! One option might be to portion out your dog's food for the day and then let her earn it throughout the day by doing certain behaviors. Or toss it into the yard and let her sniff it out. Many trainers already recommend this. This is a good way to get the behavior we want while also limiting weight gain from too many treats. And the research suggests that it may also have all kinds of cognitive and emotional benefits as well!

All these techniques are likely to have benefits at any age but given the profound impact that early experience can have on vulnerability and resilience, I suggest introducing the concept of control very early on in a puppy's life.

Provide social support

You may have heard that you should not comfort a frightened dog because it can reinforce their fear. The truth is, for social species, the presence of another animal can often improve one's ability to cope with stress. This is referred to as social support. For example, farm animals seek contact with others when they are stressed (Rault, 2012). Most of the research has looked at acute, rather than chronic, stress. However, there is some evidence that social support can help in cases of chronic stress as well (Conger et al., 1958; Westenbroek et al., 2005).

The relationship between stress and social interactions is complex. It varies depending on the behavioral test, the familiarity of the social partner, the sex of each individual and the sociality of the species.

Social animals show different stress responses when they are tested alone compared to when they are within their social group. When in the presence of other animals of the same species, social animals show a decreased response to stress and improved recovery from stress (Boissy and Le Neindre, 1997; Kikusui et al., 2006). Animals from a variety of species show less fear in a stressful situation when they are in pairs than when they are tested alone (Rault, 2012). In addition, social relationships are associated with improved immune and cardiovascular function in humans and rodents and increased life span in people, baboons, rats, and dolphins (Beery and Kaufer, 2015).

Stressed male rats spend more time together than non-stressed males (Taylor, 1981). In addition, social animals housed in pairs or groups cope better with stress (Taylor, 1981; Kiyokawa et al., 2004; Rault, 2012). Group-housed rats also showed lower levels of stress hormones in response to stress (Ruis et al., 1999). In pair-bonded prairie voles, separation from their social partner increased levels of anxiety-like behaviors and passive coping behaviors (Bosch et al., 2009; Smith and Wang, 2014). The isolated animals also showed higher levels for stress hormones than those housed with a partner (Smith and Wang, 2014).

This raises questions for dogs that are singly housed in either shelter or kennel environments. Watching the excitement that most dogs display when they see another dog on the street makes me think that most dogs simply do not get enough opportunity to interact with members of their own species. Dogs are a social species and the evidence in other animals suggest that social isolation is likely to have a negative impact on dogs and make them more susceptible to stress. This may also be true for dogs living in single-dog households. Of course, dogs also develop social bonds with people. What we don't know yet is if the human-dog bond can fully replace the dog-dog bond or if they need both.

Promoting healthy social interactions between dogs is further complicated by the fact that many dogs don't know how to interact appropriately with other dogs, or—in the worst case scenario—are dog-aggressive. This makes addressing the issues of isolation more challenging and creates a positive feedback loop where fear of aggression leads to isolation which then increases the likelihood of aggression. This is another reason for careful and consistent socialization in puppies and adolescents. This is an area where improvements to the current standard procedures for both shelter and pet dogs have the potential to have a profound impact on the stress and well-being of our dogs.

A lot of this begins with promoting regular, healthy interaction with other dogs with good social skills. This is much easier said than done because so many dogs haven't had enough exposure to other dogs. This further emphasizes the importance of starting early and continuing to maintain positive social interactions throughout adolescence. Know what good interaction looks like and how to respond when dogs aren't behaving appropriately. Know how to increase the likelihood that dogs will interact well. For example, respecting stop signals and allowing introductions on loose rather than taut leashes. Well-run puppy and adolescent socialization classes and daycare groups can also be very beneficial and a great resource for learning how to recognize healthy dog-dog interactions. I think informal play groups between friends are an excellent opportunity for socialization as well. In fact, this may be the ideal form of socialization. Dogs play in small groups with familiar dogs. They can also maintain relationships over a long period of time, rather than just the six weeks of a group class or a visit to the dog park.. In shelters, dogs can be given the opportunity to interact with other dogs as well and many facilities are now doing this.

Most of the research on social buffering has been done on interactions with other members of the same species. Can human interaction also have a buffering effect on dogs? Research suggests that this is the case as studies have shown that petting can decrease cortisol levels in dogs (Coppola et al., 2006; McGowan et al., 2018). The majority of these studies have been done on the impact of human interaction in shelter dogs and will be discussed Chapter 7.

What *kind* of social support is most beneficial? There is some evidence that it's important that the social partner is not also distressed (Kiyokawa et al., 2004; Davitz and Mason, 1955). For example, young, shy goats reacted to people with a stronger stress response when they were with an adult goat that also displayed fear (Lyons et al., 1988). If the adult goat was confident, the young goats showed lower levels of stress hormones than controls. Similar results have been found in cattle (Boissy et al., 1998) and rats (Kiyokawa et al., 2004). Researchers collected urine from the stressed individuals, then placed a sample of that urine with a test subject. They found that cattle exposed to stressed urine were slower to resume eating after a stressor and slower to explore a novel object, as opposed to cattle in the presence of urine from a non-stressed animal! To my knowledge, no one has conducted a similar study on dogs, however, it doesn't seem beyond reason to predict that scent may have a similar effect in dogs, considering how much they depend on their sense of smell. This suggests that we need to be mindful of the potential impact of the lingering scent of a frightened dog in locations where many dogs are passing through and are likely to be frightened (such as veterinary clinics and groomers).

Research on people and dogs also shows that relationship quality matters. For example, owners who described their dogs as "social partners" and "meaningful companions" had dogs with lower levels of stress hormones (Schöberl et al., 2012). Another study found that securely attached dogs had lower levels of stress hormones during separation and during play (Schöberl et al., 2016). In addition, *owners* who were insecurely attached to their dogs had dogs with higher levels of stress hormones when left alone. The challenge with these studies is that measures of stress hormones don't tell us if the dogs are experiencing good, tolerable, or toxic stress. That means we can't draw conclusions about the dogs' emotional states without additional information.

Long-term stress levels in dogs and their caretakers may be synchronized. People with higher levels of chronic stress also tended to have herding dogs with higher levels of chronic stress (Sundman et al., 2019). However, a similar study done on ancient breeds and solitary hunting breeds found no relationship between chronic stress in dogs and owners (Hoglin et al., 2021).

Sex may also be another important factor. Crowding in male rodents tends to increase measures of stress but crowding in females appears to reduce stress or have little effect either way (Beery and Kaufer, 2015). Some scientists have suggested that females respond to stress differently than males. They argue that females may take a **"tend-and-befriend"** approach, rather than just a fight-or-flight approach (Nickels et al., 2017; Taylor et al., 2000). Tend-and-befriend involves engaging in caretaking behaviors of themselves and their offspring and forming social alliances.

Sex differences in behavior in rodents are often driven by differences in sex hormones. Given that spaying and neutering removes reproductive organs involved in the production of sex hormones, it is very difficult to extrapolate evidence from intact rodents to sterilized dogs. However, it is possible that we may see differences between intact females and males. For example, there is some evidence that intact females may be more prone to fear than intact males (Puurunen et al., 2020).

It seems clear that social support can moderate stress. When our dogs experience stress, providing them with petting or play may help them cope better with that stress. It is also likely that controlling our stress levels will be beneficial for our dogs as well!

Provide enrichment

Enrichment is another factor that can improve an animal's ability to cope with stress. Enrichment can be difficult to define. Indeed, there is no single agreed upon definition within the scientific literature (Meehan and Mench, 2007). However, in general, when we refer to enrichment, we're looking for a couple factors. First, enrichment should provide an increased opportunity for animals to engage in species-typical behavior. Second, it should increase welfare in a measurable way. (Meehan and Mench, 2007; Clark, 2017).

Two types of enrichment

There are two primary types of enrichment: **physical or environmental enrichment**; and **cognitive enrichment**. Physical enrichment refers to providing animals with a complex, naturalistic environment that allows them to engage in species-typical behavior. This might include things like providing bedding for rodents to burrow in or housing social animals with other members of their own species. For dogs, this may look like providing them access to a yard, natural areas and other (friendly) dogs. I believe that giving them access to a variety of places (instead of being limited to their own home/yard) is also very important to their well-being.

Clark (2011) defines cognitive enrichment as anything that "engages evolved cognitive skills by providing opportunities to solve problems and control some aspect of the environment" and "is correlated to one or more validated measures of well-being." Here again, you see the reference to species-specific enrichment as well as improved well-being. But now we have added the additional requirements that it engages cognitive skills and increases the animal's control over the environment.

Why does cognition matter? For a long time, most scientists believed that animals were simple stimulus-response systems. In other words, something in the environment (the stimulus) would automatically trigger a behavior (the response). They believed there was no thought or intention involved. It turns out that this is more-or-less how behavior works in certain circumstances. If you've ever automatically driven to the store when you actually meant to go somewhere else or tried to turn on a light switch when you know the power is off, you are familiar with simple stimulus response mechanisms. A dog example might be a dog that runs to where her dog bed used to be, even after it has been moved, or keeps offering a previously reinforced behavior despite being asked to do a different behavior. You may remember that another word for these stimulus-response behaviors is habit. We tend to engage in habits automatically, without much thinking. However, not all behavior is habitual.

Frederick Toates (2004) uses the term "cognitions" to refer to processes that are the "result of cognitive mechanisms." Cognitions utilize higher-level control of behavior and go beyond simple stimulus-response relationships. Basically, there is more thinking involved. Planning out a route when you are running a series of errands and daydreaming about what you'll do on your next vacation are both examples of cognitions. A dog who corrects her path to the bed after it's been moved or thinks carefully about which behavior is being asked for is engaging in more cognitive processing. Cognitions allow an animal to respond flexibly to their environment and can play a role in changing stimulus-response relationships. This may be why enrichment can facilitate the development of an "active, diverse, and flexible behavioural repertoire" (Meehan and Mench, 2007). Because animals are being exposed to a variety of different experiences, they are practicing different behaviors instead of falling into repetitive habits. Remember, flexibility is a key feature of resilience, so it is easy to see why promoting flexibility can enhance well-being.

I want to examine this idea of species-typical behavior in a bit more detail. In the wild, animals face a variety of challenges on a daily basis (Shettleworth, 2010 as cited in Clark, 2011). They must find food, water, and shelter as well as avoid danger. In many cases, access to food—and sometimes water—changes on a regular basis. Food sources may move or be seasonal. There are also the challenges of accessing or capturing the food once it's been located. In addition, animals are moving through a dynamic environment that may change with weather or season. If they are a social species, they are also engaging with other members of their species. In many cases, they may even be interacting with members of other species. Feral dogs must contend with humans, of course, but also other animals such as free-ranging cats or birds that may be competing for the same food source. Successfully navigating these challenges requires a wide range of cognitive skills. That means our animals evolved to use their brains and their bodies to solve challenges throughout each day.

When we get pet dogs, we put them in a box. They have access to the outdoors, but generally only on our terms and that access is often limited. It may be restricted in terms of total time spent outside, in range (only on leash, or only in the fenced yard), or both. To make things worse, pet dogs are often punished or prevented from engaging in species-typical behaviors such as barking, digging, chewing and playing with other dogs or people. Finally, they have very limited control over many aspects of their life. If you compare this to the experience of a wild animal, I think it's easy to imagine how the lives of pet dogs—who are, in effect, captive animals—can quickly become a major concern for well-being.

Enrichment and challenges

Animals evolved to cope with challenge on a regular basis. They evolved to respond to stressful situations. We've already discussed the possibility that moderate stress during development may be beneficial. What about stress in adulthood, after the dog is fully mature? Here too, there is some speculation among researchers that not experiencing enough stress is a welfare concern. Confused? We have talked a lot about the negative effects of stress hormones. But stress hormones would not be around if they didn't also have beneficial effects. Remember, the acute stress response is *beneficial* and *adaptive*. Stress hormones also play an important role in maintaining the body's regulatory processes—therefore, too *little* stress can also become a welfare issue (Meehan and Mench, 2007).

This is where the idea of stress inoculation comes in. Chronic stress and other forms of toxic stress are bad, but a lack of stress, or **hypostimulation**, is *also* problematic and may cause animals to lose their ability to appropriately respond to challenges. Tolerable stress is okay (you could even say it's tolerable), but we really *want* good stress. The lack of good stress leads to boredom and reduced welfare. The presence of good stress can improve welfare. What we are aiming for is a striking a balance between no stress and toxic stress. Increased enrichment creates a more dynamic environment and, therefore, also increases the frequency of stressors. That's because that animal is having their status quo challenged more frequently—and that may be a good thing.

This is not just my personal opinion. There is extensive evidence to support these claims. Environment enrichment has been found to improve well-being in a variety of ways, including decreasing anxiety, reversing the impacts of maternal separation, and reducing stereotypies (Francis et al., 2002; Benaroya-Milshtein et al., 2004; Mason et al., 2007). This research has been conducted in a wide variety of animals, including dogs. For example, laboratory beagles that had access to toys and were housed with another dog performed better on cognitive tests than beagles that did not receive environmental enrichment (Milgram et al., 2005).

We have good evidence that cognitive enrichment improves well-being as well. Cattle that learned on their own to open a gate in order to get access to food, showed signs of positive excitement (Hagen and Broom, 2003). This was not seen in cattle that had access to the same food, but had the gate opened for them rather than figuring it out for themselves. McGowan and colleagues called this phenomenon the "eureka effect" (2014). It occurs when animals independently solve a problem without prior training or demonstration. In these cases, animals appear to display positive emotion (Hagen and Broom, 2004; McGowan et al., 2014).

Research on pigs has shown that increasing the complexity of the food delivery system appears to have a positive impact on welfare (Ernst et al., 2006; Puppe et al., 2007). The pigs were fitted with collars that transmitted a signal to open a box and give them access to food. However, the collars would only work if a tone had just played that indicated that it was that pig's turn to eat. They had to learn which tone was "theirs" and that the tone indicated they had access to food. Then, food (signaled by the tone) was presented at random intervals throughout the day, instead of at scheduled feeding times. This created an environment that was more cognitively challenging than simply having food handed to them at a certain time. (Remember also the benefits of learning that one's behavior is contingent). The pigs that took part in this experiment showed decreased fear and improved healing in comparison to the control group. The researchers concluded that the feeding method increased enrichment through increased cognitive activity. I also think that this set up gave pigs an increased sense of agency and this probably impacted the results as well.

Pigs given ten weeks of cognitive tasks showed improvement in several measures of welfare and well-being: reductions in abnormal behavior, increased positive emotions and increased exploration of a novel area (considered an indicator of reduced anxiety) (Puppe et al., 2007; Zebunke et al., 2013;). Similar results have been found in goats and cows (Hagen and Broom, 2004; Oesterwind et al., 2016). Research in Beagles found that they showed signs of excitement when they performed an operant task for food, human interaction, or dog interaction (McGowan et al., 2014).

There is also evidence that animals *want* challenges and enrichment. Harlow (1950) and Watson et al. (1999) found that primates would work puzzle boxes or mazes for long periods of time, even in the absence of food rewards. Research shows that animals will lever press to access novel environments and other sources of enrichment, such as bedding and raised platforms (Moon and Lodahl, 1956; Olsson and Dahlborn, 2002). This should not be surprising given how excited our dogs become when they know they are going for a walk! Other research has shown that in some cases animals will choose to work for a *reinforcer even if they have the option to attain it for free* (see Inglis, Forkman, and Lazarus, 1997 for review). You may have heard of this—it's called contra-freeloading. For example, goats will spend a significant amount of time engaging in an enrichment task (which is basically a computer game designed for goats) to earn water—even when water is freely available (Langbein et al., 2009)!

The great majority of the research in dogs has been conducted on kenneled dogs. In this case, barren environments are being compared with enrichment in the form of things like interactions with people and other dogs and interactive food toys. Therefore, these findings may not necessarily generalize to dogs living in homes where they already have access to human interaction and at least some degree of other forms of environmental enrichment. In this case, zoo animals may be a better comparison. Modern zoo animals are obviously still living in captivity, but most now have an environment that is much more enriched than the typical animal living in a kennel. Even in the case of zoo animals, increasing enrichment through activities such as training and the opportunity to forage for food has resulted in improved well-being (Coulton et al., 1997; Westlund, 2014; Hocking et al., 2015). The research on enrichment in kenneled dogs does apply to dogs living in shelter environments and will be covered in more detail in Chapter 7.

Enrichment and optimism

It's trash day and something is in the street. It's big, tall and brown and it wasn't there before! One dog may approach the trash can curiously and briefly investigate it. Another dog may pull back and slowly slink up to sniff nervously at the trash bin. These two dogs view their world in two very different ways. Animals—just like people—can be optimistic or pessimistic. If they are optimistic, they tend to anticipate reinforcement when faced with uncertainty. If they are pessimistic, they tend to anticipate punishment when faced with uncertainty (Douglas et al., 2012). This tendency toward optimism or pessimism is one type of **cognitive bias**. Cognitive biases influence perceptions in a way that changes an individual's subjective experience of the world.

The way to test it in the laboratory is to train an animal to respond to a particular cue. Researchers then teach the same animal that a different cue means they should *not* do the behavior. This is often done by teaching an animal that a bowl placed in one corner of the room will have food in it, but a bowl placed at another corner will not have food. This is called a **go/no-go** task. Cue A means "do the behavior" ("go") and Cue B means "don't do the behavior" ("no-go").

Once the animal has learned to discriminate between the two cues, they are presented with an ambiguous cue—something partway between Cue A and Cue B. For example, if the cue is the location of the bowl, the ambiguous cue may be placement halfway between the two corners. The researchers then look at what the animal does. Does the animal assume there is no reward available and withhold the behavior, or do they assume there is a reward and perform the behavior? Often, this manifests as a slower approach to the bowl, rather than no approach at all. If they withhold the behavior or approach more slowly, then that is the more pessimistic response, whereas if they perform the behavior, or approach more quickly, that's more optimistic (see diagram).

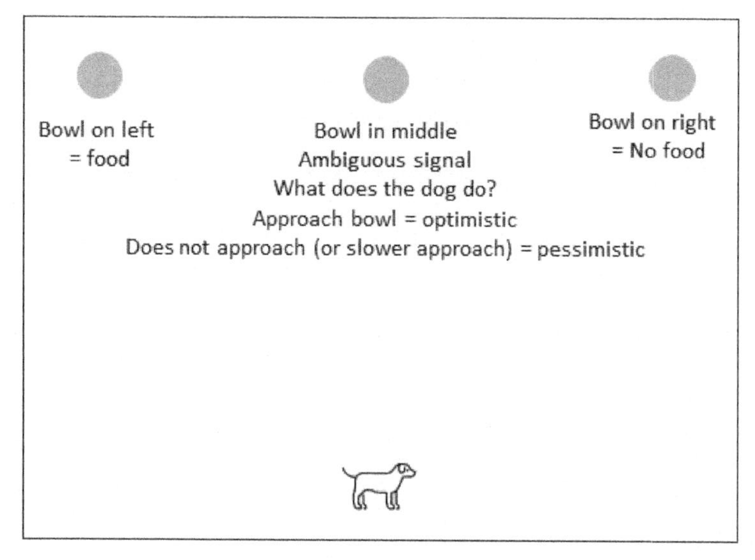

Cognitive bias

Cognitive bias is becoming increasingly popular as an objective way of assessing well-being in animals. Assessing well-being is very challenging because well-being involves the presence of "positive emotions." However, we can't know what an animal is feeling. That means we need some way of *inferring* what they might be feeling. If we want a valid method that is consistent and functional, then we need something that goes well beyond looking at the animal and deciding that they are happy (or not).

In humans, we know that there is a link between affective (emotional) state and cognition (Eysenck et al., 1991; Bar-Haim et al., 2007). People experiencing more negative emotional states focus more on threat and are more likely to interpret ambiguous stimuli in a negative light. On the other hand, people that are experiencing more positive emotions do the opposite—they are more likely to interpret ambiguous stimuli in a positive light. So, if someone shows an optimistic bias, that is one indicator that they may be experiencing positive emotional states (and vice versa). Those positive emotions increase well-being, meaning that cognitive bias is one way of assessing wellbeing. Optimism has also been associated with improved stress coping skills in people (Fontaine et al., 1993; McGarry et al., 2013).

Note that this method does involve an assumption—we still cannot ask the animals what they are feeling. We are assuming that—like people—non-human animals' interpretation of the world around them is related to their emotional state.

There have been a few studies on cognitive bias in dogs. Mendl et al. (2010) looked at the relationship between pessimistic cognitive bias and separation anxiety. They found that dogs with higher levels of separation-related behaviors also showed a more pessimistic bias. Another study looked at which personality traits were associated with positive and negative bias in dogs (Barnard et al., 2018). They found that dogs with a more optimistic bias also scored higher on sociability, excitability and non-social fear. Dogs with a more pessimistic bias scored higher on separation-related behaviors and aggression and fear toward other dogs. These studies provide support for the idea that dogs may also show a relationship between pessimistic bias and negative emotional states.

This is all very interesting, but does it really help us to help dogs? Here is where things get really interesting! It turns out that enrichment can make animals more optimistic! Research in rats, pigs and starlings has found that they are more optimistic if they are provided with cognitive and/or environmental enrichment (Douglas et al., 2012). On the flip side, rats living in an unpredictable (and therefore stressful) environment showed a more pessimistic bias (Harding et al., 2004). One study looked at the impact of nosework on cognitive bias in dogs (Duranton and Horowitz, 2019). Pet dogs practiced either nosework or heeling on a daily basis for two weeks. The dogs that engaged in nosework showed an increase in positive bias after the two-week training period. The heeling dogs, on the other hand, showed no change (they didn't become more positively or more negatively biased). This study is exciting because it's the first that I know of that looks at the impact of enrichment on pet dogs. It also demonstrates that engagement in a more species-typical behavior like foraging may be more beneficial than an activity that is cognitively challenging, but not evolutionarily relevant such as heeling. This is something I have suspected for some time, but this is the first scientific evidence of it that I am aware of.

There is also some evidence that if an animal (in this case starlings) moves from an enriched environment to a barren one, they show more pessimism than if they had been in a barren environment from the beginning (Bateson and Metheson, 2007). Dogs that were housed outside in groups and then moved to indoor solitary housing showed an increase in cortisol levels when they had been living in pleasant, sunny weather but not after the weather had been rainy (Beerda et al., 1999). It may be that transitioning from nice weather to indoor solitary housing represented a decrease in the quality of living conditions but moving from rain to solitary indoor shelter did not. This has interesting implications for animal shelters and suggests that animals coming from pet homes may struggle more than animals coming from certain other environments (such as puppy mills). If a shelter has limited resources for enrichment and can only focus on a few dogs, workers may want to selectively target animals in the shelter that come from more enriched environments.

Effective enrichment

In the wild, animals face challenges on a regular basis. These challenges impact survival and the animals have to solve them in a way that provides the greatest benefit while also minimizing any possible harm (Meehan and Mench, 2007). When we take animals away from opportunities for regular challenge, we are removing something that is central to their life. I am not recommending that we put our dogs in harm's way on a daily basis! However, I think it is very important that we remember where our animals came from and recognize that the life they now live is very different from the life they were adapted to historically.

We know enrichment is good. But what kind of enrichment do we want to provide? How can we assess the quality of enrichment programs? Several researchers (Clark, 2017; Meehan and Mench, 2017) have argued for the use of "appropriate challenge" for enrichment. Cognitive challenges should give animals the opportunity for increased control and exploration. Meehan and Mench list four possible outcomes of cognitive enrichment. We can use these outcomes to help us assess enrichment quality. The outcomes for dogs would be:

1. High skill, high challenge. The dog must apply itself to master a challenge. In people, this can result in achieving "flow" which provides a state of satisfaction and pleasure—this is the ideal!
2. Low skill, high challenge. The dog's skill level is not high enough to succeed at the challenge. This creates anxiety and frustration.

3. Low skill, low challenge. This creates apathy on the part of the dog.
4. High skill, low challenge. This results in boredom on the part of the dog.

One other aspect of appropriate challenge is giving our dogs agency, or choice and control over their environment. The best enrichment will meet the criteria of high skill/high challenge and agency. Spinka and Wemeslfelder (2011) explain why agency is so important in their concluding remarks:

> "The agency/competence complex is relevant for animal welfare for at least three reasons. First, performance of agency is directly rewarding for the animal. Secondly, when allowed its full course, agency makes the animal competent to meet high challenges with high skills, a state that has been described as fulfilling in humans, and that presumably would also be in other animals. Thirdly, highly competent animals deal with challenges more efficiently and successfully than less competent ones, and thus end up healthier and less fearful."

For dogs, this combination gives the dog control, which is reinforcing, and increases the skill set of the dog which provides her the opportunity to experience mastery over their environment (something we know to be reinforcing in people) (Nakamura and Csikszentmihalyi, 2002). It also increases the skill level of dogs which helps them navigate their world more successfully and therefore decreases stress and fear and improves emotional and physical health.

As you can see, only one of the options above—high skill/high challenge—creates a positive emotional state for the animal. Many pet dogs are likely living in one (or several) of the other scenarios—most likely low skill/high challenge and/or high skill/low challenge. Dogs have lived with humans for a long time and they appear to have developed traits that help them survive in the human world (Hare and Tomasello, 2005). However, up until recently, most dogs had a lot more freedom than they do now. In my opinion, one major source of decreased welfare in dogs is chronic frustration. They often lack the ability to engage in desired species-typical behaviors—behaviors that may be essential for well-being. This chronic frustration can result in behaviors such as destruction and increased attention-seeking behavior (often to an extreme).

When we place them in homes and provide everything for them, but also remove all control, we may be providing them with the things they need to maintain welfare from a physical needs standpoint—adequate food, water, shelter, and basic medical care—but we are not necessarily providing what they need for emotional wellbeing. Imagine Gus, a typical "Lab mix" living with a typical family. Gus gets very excited when he sees other dogs on walks and pulls hard to get to them, sometimes barking. His family hates this and yells at him to sit. They may grab him by the collar or jerk on his leash. Maybe they don't use punishment, but wave food in his face instead. Despite this, Gus continues to pull toward other dogs. This is a "low skill/high challenge" situation. No one has taught Gus a more appropriate way to behave, which means he really does not have the skills to succeed in this scenario. He is also prevented from engaging in species-typical behavior—interaction with other dogs! All of this creates anxiety and frustration in Gus. Note that this is *also* a low skill/high challenge situation for the owners and very likely creates anxiety and frustration for them as well!

Gus may also be experiencing high skill/low challenge at home. In this scenario, Gus is not getting enough cognitive enrichment. Instead, he turns to barking at passersby and stealing things around the house. In this case, Gus is a highly intelligent, complex animal, but has had little training. He now gets fewer and fewer walks because he is so difficult to manage. This results in further boredom and frustration which leads to Gus finding his own ways of entertaining himself. He then gets in trouble for "misbehaving," which places him back in that low skill/high challenge category since he doesn't know how else to get his needs met. When this "inappropriate challenge" is combined with little to no agency, it's easy to see that Gus's living situation can quickly become a major welfare concern!

The goal, then, is to provide our dogs with a challenge that is well-matched to their skills and fosters agency. That means something that is difficult, but that also allows them to use the skills they have to solve the challenge in front of them. It should also provide the animals with the opportunity to play an active role in changing their environments (Sambrook and Buchanon-Smith, 1997). Also, remember that effective enrichment should lead to improved wellbeing. However, assessing what is *actually* happening can be challenging. Again, we return to the issue of not being able to ask the animal directly, which means we have to infer their welfare state using other methods.

This checklist can serve as a guide for assessing enrichment for our dogs (and other animals).

1. Does the enrichment present a true challenge for the dog?
2. Does the dog have the skills to succeed at the challenge?
3. Does the challenge include choice and control?
4. Does the dog's welfare or well-being measurably improve?

Let's look at each of these in turn using a seek and find game and a training session as examples.

Providing a true challenge. Is this something the dog has done over and over again in this or a similar context? Do you rotate the "hide" between one of two or three locations that the dog already knows? Are you asking your dog to repeatedly perform behaviors she already knows? If the answer to these questions is yes, then the exercise may not be challenging enough for the dog. Instead, try to create a hide where the dog needs to think or engage in some trial and error before succeeding at the task. Teach a new behavior or teach an old behavior in a new context.

Matching the challenge to the dog's skill. Is the dog whining, barking or showing other signs of stress? Does the dog give up without succeeding? If the answer to these questions is yes, then the game is too challenging for the dog. You'll need to make it easier. Is the dog able to succeed without showing signs of anxiety or frustration? Have you built up the difficulty level gradually, starting with extremely easy hides or training goals? If the answer to these questions is yes, then you are on the right track!

If the dog is struggling, I don't recommend leading the dog to the hide because that would result in low skill/low challenge which also isn't desirable. Instead, place the hide somewhere easier or let the dog watch you place it, but still allow him to find it on his own. Once the dog starts succeeding again, you can gradually make the hides more difficult. The same applies to training. You have to find a goal that provides *some* challenge, but not so much that the dog becomes distressed or is unable to succeed.

Choice and control. Does the dog have the choice to opt out? Do you let the dog leave the training session if they so choose? Do you give the dog permission not to play the seek and hide game without nagging them? Do you let your dog choose their reinforcer? All of these options can help increase your dog's agency. Can you think of others?

Increased welfare/well-being. Is the dog displaying signs of positive emotion? This might look like an open-smiling face, loose body language and excitement to start the game or training session. Do you see signs of negative emotions or stress? Are you seeing a positive impact in other areas of the dog's life? Is the dog showing decreases in abnormal behavior?

Abnormal behavior is considered a sign of poor welfare. Truly effective enrichment should improve the well-being of the animal over time, not just in the moment of enrichment.

Training is considered a form of enrichment in zoos (Westlund, 2014). There is evidence that training can improve well-being in domestic animals as well. Research in cats at animal shelters showed that trained cats displayed higher levels of contentment and decreased infection rates (Gourkow and Phillips, 2016).

However, certain kinds of training may *decrease* cognitive challenge by discouraging choice and independent problem solving. Compulsion-based training that gives little to no room for creative thinking, experimentation or control on the part of the animal may not qualify as enrichment. On the other hand, shaping provides ample opportunity for cognitive challenge. This information gives us yet another argument for positive reinforcement training and providing choice to our dogs!

Aiming for high skill/high challenge may, at times, create frustration. Frustration occurs when there is a mismatch between the animals' goals and their environment (Meehan and Mench, 2007). It means they are unable to reach their goals. Dogs are likely to feel frustration when they are asked to perform a task that they cannot do. This could be because they don't have the skills in place or simply because they don't understand what is expected of them. Frustration becomes a welfare concern when animals are faced with *too much* frustration. This often occurs in the face of unsolvable problems due to high challenge, low skill scenarios which cause increased frustration and distress (Meehan and Mench, 2007).

However, frustration is not all bad—being faced with a problem that the animal is then able to solve (high skill/high challenge) decreases frustration and can increase confidence and result in positive emotions. The cows that learned to open the gate on their own appeared to experience positive emotion. In fact, learning to work through and overcome frustration can lead to **learned industriousness**.

Learned industriousness refers to the idea that effort can become associated with reinforcement such that the effort itself becomes reinforcing (Eisenberger, 1992). Think of a time when you worked very hard to achieve something. Perhaps you graduated from college, won a competition or saved money for a special trip. It took a lot of effort, but it paid off in the long run, meaning the effort itself was reinforced! Maybe next time, you'll be a little more willing to push to reach a goal. In this case, frustration may occur, but if it consistently leads to attainment of the reinforcer, the animal can learn to work through periods frustration that would otherwise be aversive. Thus, the animal learns that sustained effort is reinforcing.

In fact, there is evidence that effort and learned industriousness can improve resilience. A study by Kelly Lambert and colleagues compared rats that had to work for a reward with those that did not. The researchers built mounds of bedding in the rats' cages. During the training phase, the effort group had to find fruit loops (a favorite reward) that were buried in the mounds of bedding. Initially, the cereal was simply placed on the top of the mound. Over the course of the experiment, the cereal was slightly hidden at the top of the mound, then buried further and further down so that the rats had to work harder and search longer to get to the food. In contrast, the control group's fruit loops were placed in the open so they could be found with very little effort. This stayed consistent throughout the experiment.

After the training phase, the rats went through testing. They were taught to use a maze to find a reward (fruit loops again). Once the rats learned the maze, the experimenters took away the food reward and observed the rats' reactions. The effort-trained rats showed fewer signs of anxiety and had changes in their brains associated with increased resilience.

This suggests that positive reinforcement training that gradually increases the difficulty of the task can help our dogs cope better with stress! In essence, we are teaching them that they can do hard things. This could be achieved in several ways, including shaping and seek and hide games that gradually become more difficult. There are several important points here. First you must start with teaching dogs that their behavior matters. If they don't yet grasp this, they won't understand that they have the ability to end their frustration. Second, start small. Ask for a behavior that creates a tiny amount of frustration, then create an immediate opportunity for reward. For example, partially cover a toy (or a treat) with a blanket and ask the dog to find it. Once this is easy, cover the toy a little more. Repeat this process until the dog is eventually enthusiastically searching for the toy buried deep in the blanket. Only repeat the frustration-building exercises a few times in a row before moving on to something easier and more enjoyable. That means that the sequence above will likely progress over the course of many different training sessions. Finally, if the dog learns that every session involves frustration, training and play will likely become aversive, which is the opposite of what we want! Therefore, only work on increasing learned industriousness in a small portion of play or training sessions. (I suggest somewhere between 5 and 10%). As always, keep an eye on your dog and adjust as needed to make sure they aren't becoming overwhelmed. If at any time your dog seems distressed, the frustration is escalating, or he is giving up, make it easier.

Interactive food toys are frequently suggested as a form of enrichment in dogs. They are often used in zoos as well. Some zoo researchers have suggested that interactive food toys/puzzles are only enriching until the animal learns how to master them (Meehan and Mench, 2007). After that, they simply become physical barriers to accessing food and no longer serve as a form of cognitive enrichment. If we want to maximize the effectiveness of puzzle feeders, they should be frequently changed and updated in order to remain a dynamic challenge for the animals. One way of doing this is to hide food toys (or just food) and have the dog search for the object. Start with *very* easy hiding spots so that the dog can succeed. Then gradually increase the difficulty level as the dog gains confidence. It's also important to vary the hiding places to keep the game dynamic.

Exercise

I have an Australian shepherd. His exercise needs are through the roof. He also has some issues with becoming easily frustrated and emotionally aroused. Those issues become much more frequent and intense when he hasn't been exercised. He's a much more pleasant dog to live with when his exercise needs have been met. I have heard similar stories from countless other people about their own dogs. The saying goes, "A good dog is a tired dog," but I think there's more to it than simply being tired.

Different types of enrichment and exercise may work better for different dogs, so experiment and see what works best for your dog. One of my dogs, Darwin, thrives on training sessions and seek and find games, but doesn't care all that much for physical affection. My Aussie, Finn, is pretty much up for anything but his top two choices are play and physical touch. Find what works for your dog. When working with clients, I work very hard to find something that is enjoyable and stress relieving for the dog and the person. If the human end of the equation also enjoys the activity, they will be much more likely to do it consistently.

Exercise can help animals cope with stress. Physical activity in humans has been linked to improved mental health (Salmon, 2001). Exercised rats showed fewer anxiety- and depression-like behaviors than non-exercised rats when exposed to acute stress (Collins et al., 2009). They also show a healthier physiological response to stress (Stranahan et al., 2008). Exercise also buffers the effects of chronic stress (Miller et al., 2018). Physical activity promotes cell survival and growth (Rutten et al., 2013). This increases **neuroplasticity**, or the ability of the brain to adapt to its environment. This allows the brain to be more flexible which, in turn, increases the animal's behavioral flexibility. Remember that flexibility is an important aspect of resilience—increased flexibility leads to better coping. Exercise also improves cognition and can delay the effects of aging on the brain (Vecchio et al., 2018). Given that seniors are one group that is particularly vulnerable to stress, maintaining some level of exercise as dogs get older may be one way of decreasing their sensitivity to stress.

It is worth noting that these studies are looking at the effects of *voluntary* exercise (usually wheel running). I think this is important to remember as forced exercise takes away control and could *decrease* stress resilience. It could also increase the risk of injury. If your dog is resistant to exercise, the first step is a trip to the vet for a medical assessment!

Some of the benefits of exercise in increasing stress resilience may be related to increases in a chemical called **BDNF**. BDNF plays a key role in the growth, maturation and survival of neurons (Duman et al., 2019). Voluntary wheel running increases BDNF in the hippocampus (Lee and Soya, 2017). Furthermore, exercise before stress prevented a decrease in BDNF—as well as decreasing depression-like behavior (Russo-Neustadt et al., 2001). This suggests that exercise can counter stress in a very concrete and meaningful way.

Research in dogs shows a connection between exercise and behavior problems. Several studies have shown that exercise is associated with decreased frequency of a number of behavior issues, including fear and separation-related behaviors (Tiira, 2019). However, it's important to understand that these studies are *correlational* studies. All they can tell us is that there is a *connection* between exercise and behavior issues in dogs. They cannot tell us what is *causing* that connection. For example, it's possible that increased exercise reduces the risk of behavior issues. It's also possible that owners who exercise their dogs less often do so *because* their dogs already have behavior issues.

Exercise requires effort. Does that mean it too can improve learned industriousness? I think so. A study by Nicholas Laurence and his colleagues (2015) put rats through a seven-week exercise program. The exercise group was placed in a running ball for 20 minutes a day, five days a week. Each week, the proportion of time the rats spent running while in the ball increased. Control rats also had access to a ball, but it was stationary, so it provided no exercise.

The rats were then put through a series of tests. This included a variety of mazes, an interactive food toy and a lever pressing task. All tasks required some degree of persistence and effort in order to succeed. All rats had the option to opt out of completing any task. Across all tasks, the effort trained rats showed more persistence. This study did not look directly at resilience, but previous work (see above) has found a link between effort training and increased resilience. This may be another mechanism by which exercise increases the ability to cope with stress.

Using proper training methods

Another potential source of stress is the method used during training. Research has shown that training itself can reduce stress in dogs. However, the impact of training depends on the method used. Most of the research suggests that aversive methods are associated with increased distress and, therefore, decreased welfare in dogs. For example, Schilder and van der Borg (2004) found that German Shepherd Dogs undergoing guard dog training showed signs of immediate distress when experiencing shocks, including lowered body posture, redirected aggression and yelps, barks and squeals. The dogs trained on electronic collars (also called e-collars or shock collars), also showed more signs of stress both during the training session and outside of the training context. Another study showed that dogs trained using an e-collar showed more stress-related body language than dogs trained using positive reinforcement (Cooper et al., 2014). There was no difference between the group trained using e-collars and the positive reinforcement group in terms of effectiveness of the training. That is, they were both equally effective. These are only two studies, but a recent review on the impact of training method concluded that most of the evidence indicates that the use of aversives has a negative impact on dog welfare (Fernandes et al., 2017).

The review does highlight several limitations of the research done to date, however. Much of the research has been conducted on working dogs, such as military and police dogs. Relatively little research has focused on pet dogs. Many of the studies that have been done on pet dogs are survey based, rather than relying on objective measures. Finally, the majority of the studies have focused on the impact of e-collars, but there are other types of aversive training. In order to get a better picture about the impact of aversive training on welfare in dogs, we need research that addresses these limitations.

A more recent study does just that. de Castro et al. (2020) studied pet dogs from different training schools. They then made objective measures of the dogs' behavior and even included a cognitive bias test. Dogs were divided into one of three groups based on the methods used at the school where they were trained. The reward-based group was trained using rewards only, without any aversives. The mixed group was trained with a low frequency of punishment and the aversive group was trained with a high frequency of punishment. Dogs from the aversive and mixed groups showed more signs of disstress and were tense more frequently than dogs in the reward-based group. Furthermore, dogs in the aversive group were more pessimistic than dogs in the reward-based group. Although there are still gaps in our knowledge about the impact of aversives on welfare in dogs, there is more evidence than not that aversives cause distress in dogs. For this reason, I do not recommend aversives when training dogs.

Positive reinforcement, however, is not immune to the possibility of causing increased distress in dogs. Differences in technique can impact the dog's emotional reaction to training. Very little work has been done on this. However, one recent study tested the impact of partial reinforcement on the dog's emotional state. All dogs were trained using clickers. Dogs were divided into two groups—the 100% group where dogs received a treat after every click, and the partial reward group where dogs received food after 60% of the clicks. Both groups learned the behavior equally as quickly. However, the 60% group was more pessimistic than the 100% group. This suggests that intermittent reward, at least when paired with a clicker, may create frustration and distress in the dog. If dogs have come to expect food after the click, this makes sense as their expectation is being violated. It would be interesting to see if there are the same results when a clicker is not used. As always, remember that this is only one study, so stay tuned for more research on this topic to get a picture about what is really happening here and the best way forward.

Think about hiring a trainer

One of the best things you can do for your dog is work with a qualified, certified positive reinforcement trainer from the very beginning. These trainers can help with basic training, trouble shooting and prevention of behavior issues. Look for a trainer that treats both you and your dog with kindness and respect. You can find lists of trainers that meet minimum requirements for education and experience through the following organizations:

CCPDT – www.ccpdt.org
Certified Professional Dog Trainer, CPDT-KA or CPDT-KSA

IAABC – www.iaabc.org
Accredited Dog Trainer, ADT

If you have behavioral concerns about your dog, you'll want to look for a qualified behavior consultant. You can find lists of certified behavior consultants/behaviorists through the following organizations:

CCPDT – www.ccpdt.org
Certified Behavior Consultant Canine, CBCC-KA

IAABC – www.iaabc.org
Certified Dog Behavior Consultant, CDBC

ABS – www.animalbehaviorsociety.org /web/applied-behavior.php
Associate Certified Applied Animal Behaviorist (ACAAB, requires master's degree)
Certified Applied Animal Behaviorists (CAAB, requires PhD)

ACVB – www.dacvb.org
Board Certified Veterinary Behaviorist (DACVB, requires DVM)

Skilled application of behavior modification to extinguish fear and anxiety

What happens once the fear learning has been established? How hard is it to change that fear? The standard way of addressing fear in dogs is through a combination of **desensitization** and **counter conditioning**. That is, we expose dogs to a very low level of the fearful stimuli. It should be so low, that the dog can remain relaxed in the presence of the stimuli. If Scarlet is fearful of other dogs after being attacked, then we would start with dogs so far away that Scarlet notices them but doesn't display signs of fear or anxiety. Then we would gradually decrease the distance between Scarlet and the other dog. This process is known as systematic desensitization.

Counter conditioning is usually used in combination with desensitization. While the dog is being exposed to the very low-level fearful stimuli, we introduce something the dog loves. This is usually food. We then consistently and repeatedly pair the fearful stimuli with the enjoyable (appetitive) stimuli. Over time, the dog comes to associate the fearful stimuli with the appetitive stimuli and their emotional response starts to change.

Desensitization and counter conditioning sound straightforward, but the can be difficult to implement correctly. If you are a dog owner, the best thing you can do is to hire a qualified behavior consultant or behaviorist (see the sidebar in the previous section). However reading the information below will be helpful in understanding the research behind the methods used to change behavior in dogs.

From a learning theory perspective, counter conditioning involves two processes. We are pairing the scary stimulus (the CS) with something good (the appetitive US). This is classical conditioning. But we are also presenting the scary stimuli (the CS) without a negative consequence (the aversive US). This is extinction! (Maren and Holmes, 2016). This is important because we know a fair amount about the relationship between stress and fear extinction and the current thinking is that counter conditioning is subject to the same behavioral rules as extinction. First, let's take a detailed look at extinction.

Research has shown that extinction is very fragile. The original learning can reappear under a number of different circumstances—including the simple passage of time or being in a context other than the one where the extinction training occurred (Pavlov, 1927). We also know that when extinction occurs, the previous memory is not erased—instead, it is inhibited (Bouton, 1993). That means that when a dog goes through extinction, the previous memories are not gone. Rather, the new learning competes with the previous fear memories. These characteristics make extinction vulnerable and one of the things it is vulnerable to is stress.

Remember that when animals are stressed during the process of extinction, they show less reduction in fear and/or show more recovery of fear over time. For this reason, we need to be *extremely* mindful that we are managing stress during the counter conditioning and desensitization process. This means truly keeping the dog far enough away from their trigger that they can remain *relaxed*. This is key. When we push dogs too far, too fast, we increase their stress levels and dramatically handicap our ability to help them. In some cases, medications may be needed to reduce the dog's baseline levels of distress in order to make the counter conditioning and desensitization process more effective. In many cases, other methods to address fear and increase resilience (such as increasing exercise, enrichment and the dog's opportunities for control) will also be needed to further reduce the impacts of stress. This is especially true if the animal is fearful or anxious in many different contexts or has multiple different behavior concerns.

There is also research to suggest that the timing of extinction training matters. Researchers implemented extinction training either 15 minutes after fear learning or 24 hours after fear learning in rats (Maren and Chang, 2006). Both groups showed a decrease in the fear response—but only one group *maintained* the reduction in fear when tested again the following day. Which group do you think it was? The 15-minute group showed almost complete recovery of fear. That means the fear came back and was nearly as strong as it was before the extinction procedure. In contrast, the 24-hour group maintained the extinction learning. In other words, the rats' fear remained low over time. The researchers note that the animals in the 15-minute group were still actively showing signs of fear just prior to extinction training and they speculate that this may be why it did not work. Subsequent work has shown that the so-called **immediate extinction deficit** may last for at least six hours following the frightening experience (Maren, 2011) This suggests that if something scary happens to our dogs, we might not want to take a "get right back in the saddle" approach. Instead, it may be better to come back on another day and try again when the dog is calmer and we can introduce them to the scary thing in a more controlled and gradual manner. There is one caveat to this—if the dog is startled by an inanimate object, then recovers and chooses to approach it on her own, it is probably fine to let her do that. However, if the dog remains fearful, emotional, or wary, try again another time.

Chapter summary

We owe it to our dogs to figure out how to generate positive emotional states—the are so dependent on us for so much. Understanding how stress impacts our dogs is only part of what we need to know in order to help them. Reducing stress during development is one of the most important steps to building a resilient dog. We also need to understand how to help them cope with that stress. Increasing predictability and control can help animals cope with stress. Social support is an important factor as well. Exercise and enrichment in the form of appropriate challenge can increase resilience in dogs and improve their quality of life. Finally, make sure that you are using training methods that do not add to your dog's stress and if need be, work with professionals who are well-qualified and committed to using effective and humane methods.

This chapter covered general information about increasing stress resiliency. The next chapter discusses what we know about stress in certain populations of dogs.

Chapter 7
Stress in Specific Populations

Up until now, the book has focused on how stress generally impacts animals, especially dogs. In this chapter, we will take a detailed look at stress in specific populations and contexts. First, we'll discuss stress in shelter dogs and how we might reduce it. Then, we'll examine what we know of stress in performance and working dogs, including how characteristics of the handler may influence the dog's stress level.

Shelter dogs

Rosco was just surrendered by his family. He was a 10-month-old, 50-ish pound mixed breed and his energy and excitement were just too much for the family to handle. Now, he is alone in a loud, unfamiliar place with few of the comforts of home. The people are always kind to him, but he rarely gets to go outside, play or spend time with people. When people approach his kennel, he gets extremely excited, but they often continue without stopping or only briefly interact with him. What kind of impact does shelter living have on dogs? What can shelters do to attempt to mitigate that stress?

Are shelter dogs chronically stressed?

Quite a few studies have been done on stress in shelter dogs, namely looking at how shelter living impacts stress hormones. Looking at the studies as a whole, it is clear that entering a shelter increases stress hormone levels in dogs (Protopopova, 2016; Hennessy et al., 2020). However, this increase usually only lasts for several (7 to 10) days before the stress levels decrease to baseline (Protopopova, 2016). In addition, studies have not found evidence of differences in stress hormone levels between dogs that have been housed at a shelter for short- versus long-term stays (Titulaer et al., 2014; Walker et al., 2016). Interpreting these results is complicated.

We can probably conclude that entering a shelter is stressful given the increase in stress hormone levels. However, what does this mean? Measuring stress hormone levels does not directly tell us about the dog's emotional state. Stress hormone levels tell us if the dog is acutely stressed, but they don't tell us what *kind* of stress the dog is experiencing. That is, stress hormone levels can't indicate whether the stress is good, tolerable, or toxic. Exercise, for example, may increase stress hormone levels (Mastorakos et al., 2005). Stress hormones are also influenced by a number of factors other than stress. For instance, time of day, sampling method, age and surgical sterilization have all been found to influence stress hormone levels (Chmelikova et al., 2020).

For these reasons, it is best if assessments of stress in shelter dogs supplement measurements of stress hormones with additional methods. Examples include observations of body language and cognitive bias testing. Having said that, most of the studies on stress in shelter dogs have focused on stress hormone levels, which is why I focus on that here.

It is also difficult to interpret the decrease in cortisol levels after several days at the shelter. Does this mean that the dogs are no longer stressed? It's possible that after several days the dogs habituate to the shelter life and the reduction in cortisol reflects that they are, in fact, less stressed. However, there are several other possible explanations as well.

Remember way back to Chapter 2. There, I explained that under conditions of chronic stress, the stress response system can become dysregulated. That means it's no longer functioning correctly. In this case, you may get an increased production of stress hormones, but it's also possible to see a decreased production of stress hormones. Therefore, it's possible that the change in stress hormone levels in shelter dogs is actually a sign of dysregulation of the HPA axis, which is a sign of chronic (toxic) stress (Protopopova, 2016). Some studies have shown support for the idea that the stress response in shelter dogs is dysregulated, but others have not (Hennessy, 2013).

The numbers reported in these studies represent the average stress hormone levels across all dogs. That means the stress hormone level for each dog is pooled together to come up with one number. This is necessary in order to run statistics, but it also has the effect of obscuring individual differences. Imagine we're looking at the age of shelter dogs. In one (very small) sample, we may have dogs that are one, five, and 12 years old. In a second sample, we may have a four, six and eight year old and in the third sample we may have three dogs that are all six years old. In each case, the average age of the dogs is six years! It's clear that looking at just the average does not provide a complete picture of each individual. The evidence from other research on stress resilience tells us that there are individual differences in how animals cope with stress in general. We also have a few studies on dogs that provide some insight into possible individual differences in shelter dogs.

First, as mentioned before, stress hormone levels are influenced by factors such as neuter status and time of day. As discussed in Chapter 5, coping style, or personality, may affect how well a dog copes with stress. Bold animals tend to cope with stress better, while shy animals do not cope as well. In addition, several of the studies on shelter dogs excluded dogs that were aggressive or particularly fearful (for example, Hennessy et al., 1997). It's possible that those dogs were having the most difficulty coping with the stress and that, by excluding them, the studies captured primarily the dogs that were better able to cope with the shelter environment.

We have some evidence that lends credence to this hypothesis. Titulaer et al. (2013) did one of the few studies that found that stress hormone levels were still high after the first couple weeks. In this case, levels remained high after six months. However, in this study dogs were not excluded based on behavior. Another study found that stress hormone levels increased over a 10-day period for dogs that were surrendered by their owner and did not have prior experience in the shelter (Hiby et al., 2006). Also remember that a change from an enriched environment to a more barren environment can have even more of a negative impact than simply being in a barren environment from the beginning. Those dogs may struggle more in a shelter environment. However, for some dogs, entering the shelter may actually be an improvement over their previous situation. If they were stray or living in a neglectful or abusive environment, the shelter may provide consistent shelter, food, water and protection from physical harm that their previous living situation did not. These dogs may actually experience an increase in welfare upon entering the shelter.

We can also get some insight from research that has been done on laboratory animals and dogs in non-shelter settings. As outlined in previous chapters, predictability and control are major factors in how distressing a particular experience is. It's hard to imagine that a dog in a shelter wouldn't have less control than dogs in most pet homes. Depending on the shelter, the environment may be more or less predictable than a pet home. We also know that social isolation is a source of stress. It also prevents access to the beneficial effects of social interaction. The amount of isolation will vary among different shelters and different dogs.

We still need more research before we'll have a clear picture of how time spent in the shelter impacts the behavior and welfare of dogs. However, there are two things we can take from this data. First, these results suggest that entering the shelter is a stressful experience for dogs. After that, it seems likely that whether the dogs experience chronic stress depends on several factors including their individual coping styles, their personal history and the qualities of the shelter. We still do not have enough data to definitively say if the shelter is a stressful environment in general, but it seems safe to say that the type of stress is going to vary from individual to individual. For some dogs, the shelter environment will produce toxic stress. For others it will be tolerable, or they may habituate to the environment over time to the point where the shelter is no longer stressful for those dogs.

Second, these data give us some insight into which dogs may be at higher risk for experiencing toxic stress and decline in welfare. In an ideal world, all dogs would be recipients of enrichment programs, but not all shelters have the resources to work with every dog. In those cases, dogs that are especially at-risk can be prioritized for stress-reducing enrichment programs.

The first consideration is age. The impact on pregnant mothers, young (juvenile and adolescent) dogs and seniors is likely to be even more dramatic. As we've already seen, stress during development leads to a number of behavior issues down the road. To further complicate the picture, these issues don't always manifest until adolescence or adulthood, meaning that dogs may seem emotionally healthy and stable at adoption, only to decline later. The stress of the shelter environment may accelerate age-related cognitive decline in older dogs.

Shelter staff can also look at a dog's coping style. Dogs that show a more reactive and avoidant response may be more at risk for chronic distress during the shelter stay. Finally, dogs that come from pet homes may be more at risk than those picked up stray. All of this is speculative. What we really need is more research on this topic, so we have more data to back up shelter policies and procedures.

Now that we've discussed what we know of the impact of stress on shelter dogs, the next step is understanding how we can intervene to try to decrease stress—or improve a dog's ability to tolerate it.

Reducing stress in shelter dogs

Many of the interventions already discussed in this book can be applied to shelter dogs. However, it is always nice to apply practices that are evidence-based. This is not always possible in the dog world, but in this case, there are quite a few studies on decreasing stress in shelter dogs.

Most studies have found that human interaction decreases stress in shelter dogs. This is based on physiological and behavioral measures of stress (Hennessy et al., 1997; Coppola et al., 2006; McGowan et al., 2018). Stress hormone levels often decrease even if the person does not interact with the dog and instead sits passively without engaging (Shiverdecker et al., 2013). Many of these studies also incorporate some kind of physical exercise, but the reduction in stress occurs even in the interactions does not involve physical exercise (Shiverdecker et al., 2013; Hennessey et al., 2013).

There are a couple variables that may influence how effective human interaction is at reducing stress. Hennessey et al. (1997) found that stress hormone levels were not impacted by petting sessions if the petter was a man. Upon further investigation, they realized that men and women used different styles of petting (Hennessy et al., 2020). When men were taught to pet the dog in a calmer manner, they became as effective at reducing stress hormone levels as female petters (Hennessy et al., 2020)! The location of the social interaction setting may also be important. One study showed that sessions were most effective if they take place in a quiet room away from the hustle and bustle of the shelter (Shiverdecker et al., 2013). So far, these studies have found that the reductions in stress hormone levels are relatively short-lived suggesting that the dogs need daily human interaction.

Training may also help. Kiddie et al. (2015) found that training dogs less than once a day was associated with decreased well-being scores. On the other hand, well-being was increased by the presence of dog beds, staff interaction, exercise, training 30 minutes or more each day, and access to a quiet environment.

Working and performance dogs

In addition to research on stress in shelter dogs, there have been a handful of studies on therapy, working and performance dogs.

Therapy dogs

There have been several studies on stress in therapy dogs. The research focuses on two particular kinds of intervention: animal-assisted therapy (AAT) and animal-assisted activity (AAA). Kruger and Serpell (2006) define AAT as animal-assisted interventions where professionals in the field use therapy dogs and other animals to achieve a particular goal in a treatment setting. For example, a dog may be used in a physical therapy session to help patients engage in particular movements as part of their treatment. In contrast, AAAs are defined as activities with no specific goal or outcome in mind and that can be conducted by volunteers who are not professionals in that field (Kruger and Serpell, 2006). The latter is what we usually think of when we think of therapy dog work.

Several studies have been done on the use of AAT and AAA dogs, referred to as "therapy dogs" for the remainder of this chapter. Some studies compare measures of stress in dogs in the home setting with measures of stress in the therapy session. Others attempt to assess stress levels before and after a therapy session. Several studies look at both. The results of the studies have been mixed. Some studies have found that stress hormone levels increase after therapy sessions, whereas others have found no change or a decrease (see Glenk, 2017 for review).

Why are the results so variable? There are several reasons we may see these differences. Many of these studies are small (often fewer than 20 dogs). That means that the results are easily skewed in one direction or the other if you happen to get a higher than average number of dogs with certain characteristics. Let's say that you have a box of 100 marbles. 50% are blue and 50% are green. These are the actual population numbers. However, if you reach into the box with your eyes closed, you will draw different percentages of marbles. If you sample 98 marbles, your numbers will very closely resemble the actual sample number. However, if you only took out four, it's entirely possible the numbers will be skewed. By chance, you may end up with three blue and one green, or even four blue and zero green (or vice versa). This means that the sample is not representative of the actual population. You can see that this is much more likely to happen if the sample is small, so it may be that the small samples in the therapy dog studies are not always accurately representing the larger population. If that's the case, then—depending on how representative the sample is—one could get varying results just based on chance. Note that this is not a criticism of the authors themselves—recruiting dogs for research studies can be very difficult, so there are often logistical reasons that keep the numbers small.

Another major issue is that therapy dog programs are not standardized. That means that the training and selection process for dogs and handlers and the procedures and policies at the facilities may vary widely from study to study. In addition, therapy dogs work with a wide variety of populations. Examples of populations used in these studies include inpatient addiction treatment patients in a program where the therapy dog handler is also a trained drug treatment professional, children with cancer, and adults with fibromyalgia or chronic fatigue syndrome (Glenk et al., 2014; McCullough et al., 2018; Clark et al., 2020). (In case you're curious, stress hormone decreased after sessions in the substance abuse treatment dogs and showed no change in the other two groups.)

Research on stress and well-being in therapy dogs is only just beginning. It is not uncommon to get conflicting results early on in the research process. There are many different factors that may influence the results and, at the beginning of the research process, there is often not enough information to accurately identify all the important factors. For example, there is some evidence that stress is increased in dogs that have a long car ride to get to the facility (de Carvalho et al., 2020) and that it is decreased in more experienced therapy dogs (King et al., 2011). As more research is done, we will gradually get a clearer picture of whether these or other factors play an important role in moderating the stress levels of therapy dogs.

Also remember that stress hormone levels alone do not tell us anything about the dog's *emotional* state. They simply tell us if the dogs are experiencing acute stress, not whether it is good, tolerable or toxic. Therefore, in order to draw conclusions about the dog's well-being, we need more information. Many of the studies have also looked at other physiological and behavioral signs of stress, such as heart rate and body language. Unfortunately, as of right now, those results are also somewhat inconclusive, though it's worth noting that none of the studies have found some clear and obvious signs of distress in therapy dogs (Glenk, 2017).

We also need to remember that the population does not represent the individual. Though we don't have evidence of obvious distress in therapy dogs, that does not mean that it is not present in certain individuals, or higher in certain populations of dogs or within certain facilities. Not all therapy dog programs are the same. I have personal knowledge of multiple incidents of displays of fear and aggression in therapy dogs where I feel there was a welfare concern with certain individual dogs. Other dogs appear to thrive in a therapy setting. The International Association of Human-Animal Interaction Organization, the American Veterinary Medical Association and Pet Partners all emphasize that therapy dogs should enjoy the interactions (Clark et al., 2020).

We still need further research to provide clear and complete guidance on policies and procedures regarding therapy dogs. However, in a recent review of research on animal-assisted interventions, Glenk (2017) provided a list of recommendations for working with therapy dogs. She states that training of therapy dogs should utilize positive reinforcement and that dogs should never be forced to interact with recipients. Further, dogs should be given time to explore the setting and become comfortable in the new environment. They should be given free access to water as well as to a quiet space. Room temperatures should be kept at a moderate level. These guidelines provide a good starting point and can be built on as more research is conducted in this area.

Working dogs

Working dogs are dogs that spend much of their time completing tasks for the benefit of humans. Police dogs, working farm dogs, assistance and guide dogs are all examples of working dogs. There is limited research on working dogs. Much of what has been done focuses on early development and has already been discussed in those sections of the book. However, a handful of studies have been done on the effects of the work itself on stress in working dogs. Much of this research has focused on the relationship between the handler and the dog. Research on search and rescue dogs in Poland (Wojtaś et al., 2020) found that stress hormone levels of the dogs and handlers were higher after the certification exam than before the exam. There was also a positive correlation between stress hormone levels in handlers and their dogs. That means if stress levels were high in the handler, they also tended to be high in their dogs, and vice versa. Remember that all this tells us is that there is a relationship between dog and handler stress. It does *not* tell us about the cause of that relationship.

When the same study analyzed the results by sex, they found that there was a correlation between female dogs and female handlers, but no correlations with male dogs and male handlers. Similar results were found in a study by Sundman et al. (2019) that looked at correlations between long-term stress in dogs and owners. This suggests that female dogs may be more susceptible to stress in their owners, but we need more research to confirm this possibility. Another study (Lit et al., 2010) measured stress hormone levels in handlers and measured pulse and temperature in the dogs. They found that the handlers' stress hormone levels were associated with the dog's pulse and temperature as well as the handlers' ratings of their dog's stress level.

An Italian study (Diverio et al., 2016) examined the effect of a mock avalanche rescue exercise on measures of stress in military search and rescue dogs. The measurements included stress hormone, heart rate and temperature. In all dogs, the search lasted 10 minutes or less and in addition to the search itself, the dogs were transported to the site via helicopter. All measures increased from pre-test to post-test. However, by two hours after the test, all measures except stress hormone levels had returned to baseline. Stress hormones levels decreased as well but had not fully reached baseline at the last testing point, which was two hours after the mock search. The researchers concluded that the dogs' welfare was not negatively impacted.

The working dog studies have all of the same limitations as the therapy dogs, including variations in context and small sample sizes. In the case of the working dogs, physical exertion is an additional factor as moderate-to-intense exercise alone can increase stress hormone levels (Angle et al., 2009). This further complicates the interpretation of the results.

Performance dogs

Any dog that competes in a dog sport (such as agility, flyball or competitive obedience) is a **performance dog**. A handful of studies have been done on stress in performance dogs. Pastore et al. (2011) looked at stress hormones and behavioral measures in agility dogs before and after a run and found the stress hormones were higher after the run. They also found that before, during and after the run, the dogs exhibited restlessness and that before the run they showed trembling, panting and tail wagging (tail wagging is considered a sign of arousal). During the run, dogs displayed circling behavior—particularly when they arrived at an obstacle prior to receiving direction from the handler. After the run, dogs performed a body shake which often occurs after a stressful experience. Remember that these findings do not mean that every behavior occurred in every dog, but that as a group, the behaviors mentioned happened more frequently at the time point described. In this case, the authors concluded that agility competition was stressful for dogs. However, they also point out that stress is subjective, so a dog that is experiencing stress is not necessarily having a *negative* experience.

Buttner et al. (2015) examined the relationship between stress hormone levels in humans and dogs during agility competition. Similar to working dogs, a positive correlation was found between stress hormone levels in dogs and their handlers. There was also a positive correlation between human stress hormone levels and affiliative behavior shown by the handler to the dog after the race. That means that handlers with high stress hormone levels were more friendly to their dogs after the run. This is consistent with the "tend-and-befriend" hypothesis mentioned earlier—when stressed, women may become more affiliative. Three quarters of the study participants were women. Perhaps surprisingly, there was not a relationship between affiliative and punitive behavior from the handler to the dog and the dog's stress hormone levels. In other words, friendly or punishing behavior was not associated with changes in stress hormone levels in the dogs.

Finally, dogs handled by men showed greater increases in stress hormones after competition than dogs handled by women. It's important to note, however, that there were only fourteen dogs handled by men, compared to 44 handled by women. Remember our small sample size discussion from earlier—it's possible that the fourteen dogs handled by men just happened to be dogs that also had a stronger stress response. However, another study shows that there may be an interaction between testosterone levels in men and stress hormone levels in dogs after an agility trial (Jones and Joseph, 2006). Men's pre-run testosterone levels were positively correlated with changes in the dog's stress hormone levels after the run, but only in losing teams. In addition, men who showed a greater decrease in testosterone levels after a loss also had dogs with higher levels of stress hormone post-run. In winning teams, there was no relationship between men's testosterone levels and the changes in the dog's stress hormone levels. This is a very interesting finding that deserves more research, particularly given the connection between testosterone and dominance but, unfortunately, at the time of writing, no follow-up studies had been published on this topic.

One thing that stands out clearly from this research is that the humans' emotional state and stress levels impact their dogs.

Chapter summary

We need much more research on shelter, working and performance dogs to get a complete picture of resilience and stress coping in these groups. However, the fact that we have any data is worth celebrating as it is only in the last 10 to 20 years that this research has been available. If you pay close attention to the date of the studies cited in this chapter, you will see that almost all of them are from this century. We are just beginning this research and I believe that there is much more to come! It is a very exciting time to be in our field as I believe that the number of dog studies will continue to grow. This influx of scientific evidence has the power to catapult our field to new heights that we couldn't have imagined 20, or even 10, years ago!

There is still a lot about stress in these populations that we do not know. It would have been possible to leave this information out given how muddy the picture is at the time of this writing. However, I think it is important to have a solid understanding of what we do and don't know when it comes to stress in dogs. I also feel it's important to understand how difficult it is to interpret these studies and that we need to be cautious in how we apply them to real-world contexts.

The research that has been done so far is a necessary and essential first step. We first need to establish that dogs in these scenarios are stressed before we can look more closely at what type of stress they are experiencing and what factors influence the type of stress.

Perhaps the question is not so much "are these dogs experiencing stress," but "what kind of stress are they experiencing" and, perhaps most importantly, "what factors allow us to predict which dogs are most likely to experience tolerable or toxic stress and what can we do to mitigate those factors." It is my fervent hope that in the next few decades we will have a much better answer to the last two questions than we do now. Although I am speaking about the specific populations of dogs covered in this chapter, these statements also apply to research on stress and dogs in general.

Chapter 8
Concluding Thoughts

This book has covered what we currently understand about how stress impacts behavior. It's important to remember that this is only a tiny snapshot of the work that has been done on the impacts of stress during early development and on through to a dog's senior years. People spend their entire careers dedicated to researching one small aspect of this topic so the information in this book is oversimplified by necessity. There is also a lot about stress and the development of resilience that we still do not understand. That does not mean the information we do have is not useful, but I want to make sure my readers understand the experience of stress is not the absolute final word—or the full story—on behavior. Here are some other things to think about.

Details matter. As I mentioned before, the exact results depend on several factors. The timing of stress matters. Stress at different ages will have slightly—or dramatically—different impacts. The type, intensity and duration of stress matters. Obviously, chronic stress has different impacts than acute stress. Mild stress also has different impacts than severe trauma. Unfortunately, many of the details are beyond the scope of this book, but it is important to know that these differences exist.

Gender matters. Most of the studies on rodents are done in males. This is because females go through an estrus cycle which complicates study design and analysis. Of course, the difficulty with focusing primarily on males is that it creates a bias in the data. As discussed earlier, it's possible that males and females respond differently to stress. In fact, quite a few studies have found different results between males and females.

Genetics matter. The environment that any one animal experiences is always filtered through their genetics. So, how an individual reacts to the world around them is going to be interpreted and responded to based on their genetic make-up. It's that unique interaction between genetics and the environment that will ultimately determine behavior.

Learning matters. If you work to change behavior in dogs, then this is one thing that has probably been etched into your brain—learning matters. Through classical conditioning, dogs can develop negative or positive associations with a wide variety of triggers. They become excited to see the leash but run from the nail clippers. We can also intentionally train a wide range of behaviors using instrumental conditioning. The things dogs experience in their lives (including both things we intentionally and *un*intentionally teach them) impact their behavior. But, this learning is still filtered through early development (which changes brain structure and function) and genetics. That means we will be able to make more progress with some dogs than others.

Finally, individual differences matter. What this is really saying is that each animal is a sample of one. Each animal is a unique combination of genetics, early experience, learning and other factors that will uniquely impact how that specific individual perceives and interacts with the world around him or her. The research I cover in this book is useful for understanding dog behavior as a whole and can be an excellent tool for guiding the prevention and treatment of behavior problems in dogs—as well as for generally improving their quality of life. But you still have to work with the dog in front of you. Some dogs will have a traumatic experience and come through it relatively stable and healthy, other dogs will be so impacted that they are never able to fully recover and live a normal life. Most dogs will probably be somewhere in between. In Chapter 5 we talked more about the influences on vulnerability and resilience to stress.

Knowledge is empowerment. Take this information and use it to make a difference!

I hope that reading this book has presented you with a new angle for understanding and approaching behavior in dogs. It should provide you with several additional tools for addressing behavior problems that may result from the impacts of stress in dogs. Perhaps more importantly, you should now also have several new ideas for preventing behavior issues in dogs, as well as for increasing their quality of life. We all know stress impacts behavior, but I hope you now have a much deeper understanding of exactly how it impacts behavior. My goal is to provide you with hope about how much *more* we can do to help dogs. Take this information and use it to make a difference. Research on dogs is continuing at a rapid pace and the more we know, the more equipped we'll be to give them the best lives possible. Keep learning, keep growing, keep innovating and keep improving on how you train, interact and live with dogs. They will thank you for it and you will have made the world a better place.

Appendix: Science!

There is a lot of information in this book. You likely noted the many citations I included in the text. Knowledge is a powerful thing. However, one critical aspect of learning is understanding how to assess, interpret and appropriately apply new information. When it comes to science, that means understanding the scientific process itself. I put together this appendix so that you can better draw your own conclusions about research you may read. Just because something appears in a book or a journal does not mean the data cannot be evaluated differently. In addition, new research will always be coming out and I hope this information will help you to understand and correctly interpret and apply that research.

If you'd like an easy way to stay up-to-date on this research and how it applies to living and working with dogs, you'll love my monthly *Research Bites* webinars. Each month I summarize a recent dog behavior study and as a group we discuss the implications of the results and how to use the information in dog training and behavior work! The information is available through my website, www.sciencemattersllc.com. I also offer multi-week courses on the science of behavior.

It is difficult to overstate the importance of having a solid foundation in the scientific method. The animal training and behavior field is now being flooded with research. This is a wonderful thing because professionals in the field are increasingly able to use methods that are truly evidence-based. However, the increase in availability of scientific research in the field also increases the importance of being able to correctly interpret and apply those research studies.

As access to information continues to grow, more and more trainers and behavior consultants will rely heavily on this research to improve their success rates. I believe that a strong understanding of scientific principles, combined with on-the-ground real world experience, will catapult our profession to exciting new heights in terms of our ability to help animals and their people. A misunderstanding of science can cause one to misinterpret scientific findings and dismiss or over apply them to the detriment of the dogs they are trying to help. Professionals that do not keep up-to-date with the current research—or who apply it incorrectly or ineffectively—will struggle to keep up with those who have a solid foundation in interpretation and application of research.

You will be much better at your job if you can sort through all the new information to determine what is valid and how and when to apply research findings to real-world work with dogs. This section will help you put the rest of the information in this book—and in the research world in general—into the proper perspective. This will allow you to use it as effectively as possible and will help you achieve more effective results with the dogs in your life.

Guiding principles of scientific research

Let's talk about the guiding principles of the scientific approach itself. Science is based on **induction** rather than **deduction**. What's the difference? Deduction involves developing a specific conclusion from general premises. For example:

Premise 1: All aggression in dogs is caused by dominance

Premise 2: Buster bit someone.

Conclusion: Therefore, Buster is dominant.

Deduction allows us to come to a logical conclusion based on the premises. However, *it only works if the premises are true*. If one or more of the premises are false, then the conclusion is likely to be false as well. In this case, premise one is false. How often does this happen with dogs? Here is another example:

Premise 1: Dogs are capable of feeling guilt.

Premise 2: When dogs do something wrong, they feel guilty.

Premise 3: When a dog hangs his head, puts his ears back and looks up at you, that means he is feeling guilty.

Conclusion: Therefore, if you come home and your dog looks guilty, that means he's done something wrong, and he knows it was wrong.

Both of these conclusions make sense logically—if you accept the premises they are based on. But what are we basing those premises on? How do you know they are true? In fact, we don't have any convincing evidence that dogs are feeling guilt in this context. They may seem correct, but how do you know? The answer is that you *don't* know, unless you test them.

This is where science comes in. Science is based on inductive reasoning. Induction involves inferring a general conclusion from specific, observable data. For example:

Observation: Dogs under chronic stress are more anxious.

Conclusion: Chronic stress causes anxiety.

Testing conclusions and forming a theory

Now that you have a conclusion, you need to test it. The next step is to develop the conclusion into a question in the form of a hypothesis. Hypotheses are specific and testable. One of my graduate school professors, Dr. Chris Wagner, always emphasized that a good hypothesis is expressed as an if:then statement. *If* chronic stress causes anxiety, *then* animals exposed to chronic stress should show an increase in anxiety. That is specific and you can test it. You could make it more specific, of course, by specifying how and for how long the animals would be stressed and how we would measure the stress and the anxiety. The 'how' is covered in the methods section of scientific papers.

Once many hypotheses have been tested and large amounts of evidence have been gathered, scientists may form a **theory** about a particular concept. Good theories have a several important qualities:

1. They are based on large amounts of data.
2. They explain *why* something is happening.
3. They make testable predictions.

The last point is particularly important because it means two things: 1) the theory generates new hypotheses and new research; and 2) it's **falsifiable**. That is, it is specific enough that it is clear what evidence would be needed to disprove it.

Note that I am talking about *falsifying*, rather than *proving*, a theory (or hypothesis). That's because you can never know something with absolute certainty—it's always possible there is an exception out there somewhere. However, it is possible to *dis*prove a hypothesis or theory. If you disagree with a particular theory, figure out what evidence would be required to disprove it and then go out and test it. Let's go back to the deductive reasoning example on dominance. Here it is again:

Premise 1: All aggression in dogs is caused by dominance.

Premise 2: Buster bit someone.

Conclusion: Therefore, Buster is dominant.

Let's say you disagree with the first premise or the conclusion. How would you disprove it? Assuming we have clear evidence that Buster bit someone, then the thing to focus on would be "Premise 1: All aggression is caused by dominance." There are many ways you could test this, but here are a few. You could test whether or not domestic dogs establish dominance hierarchies (a linear rank-ordering of group members where higher-ranked individuals have priority access to resources compared to lower-ranked individuals). If they don't develop dominance hierarchies, then that negates premise one right there. If they do, you could test whether or not dominant individuals are more aggressive. Or, if you found evidence of something other than dominance driving aggression, that would also disprove the conclusion. Make sense? (Note that dominance and it's impact on behavior is complex—see the section on generalization below for more information.

Scientific methods

It's also helpful to have a general understanding of basic methodology. What is correlation and what can it tell us? What's the difference between correlational and experimental studies? What are controls?

Correlational studies

First, you should understand the differences between **correlational** and **experimental studies**. Correlational studies look for relationships between different variables, but they do not attempt to manipulate the experience of the research subjects. For example, you might go into a shelter and measure stress levels in shelter dogs and then determine if there is a relationship between length of time in the shelter and levels of stress hormones. Or, you could test whether stress levels are lower in dogs whose trainers reward more often. Remember—there is no manipulation here. The researcher is simply making observations. In other words, no one is telling the trainers to reward more or less. The scientist is just looking at what trainers naturally do, and then seeing if they can find a relationship between rate of reinforcement and measures of stress in the dogs.

If there is a relationship between the two variables, then they are said to be **correlated**. Correlations can be **positive** or **negative**. If the correlation is positive, that means both factors increase in the same direction. As height increases, weight also tends to increase. If the correlation is negative, that means the factors tend to move in opposite directions. For example, as age increases, memory tends to decrease.

Correlational studies are valuable because they are easier to set up and allow us to study things that would normally be unethical to study, but are important nonetheless. For example, a correlational study allows us to examine the effects of abuse on dog behavior without putting some dogs in an 'abuse' group where they would be intentionally abused for the purposes of the study. Obviously, this would be unethical! Instead, you could look at dogs that came from an abusive situation and compare them with dogs living in homes where they are treated well.

The major drawback of a correlational study is that we cannot infer **causation**. That is, a relationship between X and Y does not *necessarily* mean that X causes Y or that Y causes X. It's possible that there is a causal relationship, but it's also possible they are both influenced by a third factor, or it could just be chance.

For example, the Sundman study cited earlier found that long-term stress level in owners was positively correlated with long-term stress levels in herding dogs (Sundman et al., 2019). That means owners with higher levels of chronic stress had dogs that also had higher levels of chronic stress.

However, we cannot assume from these results that the owner's stress is *causing* the dog to be more stressed. It's possible it is. Owners under stress might be more likely to punish the dog or might simply be too busy to provide adequate exercise and enrichment. But it's also possible that stressed dogs are increasing the owners' stress. A dog under high stress may be more difficult to live with, and that could be increasing the owner's stress, particularly if they don't know how to address the dog's behavior. Alternatively, there could be some third factor, like limited resources, that's contributing to the stress in both the person and the dog (due to poor health care, not enough food, etc.) I'm sure you can come up with other possible explanations as well. If we wanted to test whether owner stress causes increased stress in dogs, then we would need to conduct an experimental study that put some people in a group where they experienced something distressing for a long period of time (weeks or more) and compare their dogs to dogs of owners that were not chronically stressed. Given what we know about the impacts of chronic stress, this would be unethical which is why we have correlational data rather than experimental data for this study!

Here is another example taken from the *Spurious Correlations* website run by Tyler Vigen (well worth a visit if you'd like to see more examples of surprising correlations).

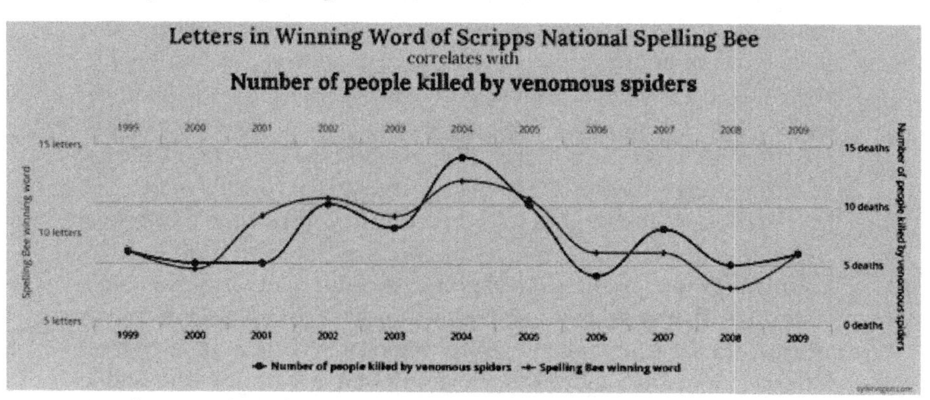

Looking at this chart, you can see that over the course of 10 years (1999 - 2009), the number of deaths from venomous spiders positively correlates with the number of letters in the winning word of the Scripps National Spelling Bee. That is, as the number of letters in the winning word increased, the number of deaths from venomous spiders also increased, and vice versa.

I think we would all agree that the number of letters in the winning word does not *cause* people to be bitten and killed by venomous spiders (or vice versa). We have to be very careful to avoid assuming that factors that are correlated have a causal relationship. This was drilled into my head as a student, and I will repeat it here—correlation does not equal causation. Correlation does not equal causation. Correlation...okay, you get the idea! If you want to look at the cause of a behavior or phenomenon, then you have to run an experimental study. Period.

Experimental studies

In experimental studies, the researcher *is* manipulating one or more factors. Maybe they are adding playtime to one group of shelter dogs to see if it reduces stress, or randomly assigning certain dogs to a high reward group and others to a low reward group. In this case, because the researcher is manipulating one specific thing and keeping everything else constant, much stronger conclusions can be made regarding causation. If everything is kept the same in the shelter dogs except adding a play group, then any differences between the groups are most likely due to the addition of play.

This isn't quite the end of the story, though. There are a few other things to be considered. It turns out that science—just like life—is complicated. Let's go back to the play group example. Imagine the shelter measures stress levels in dogs, then adds a play session for every dog in the shelter. After a couple weeks, they measure the stress levels again and find that they've decreased. Great! That means that play decreased the stress, right? Well, not so fast. If *all* dogs had the same experience, how do we know it was play that actually mattered? Maybe the dogs showed less stress because they adjusted to the shelter environment. In order to isolate the effects of play, you want to have a **control group**. In the control group, conditions are kept the same as normal. That is, there is no manipulation; the group just continues as usual. In the experimental group, some factor is manipulated. So, for this study, you might have one group that gets played with and a control group that sticks to the normal routine.

So far, we've discussed experimental design, but this is only half of the equation. Now let's look at how to interpret and apply research results. This is the part that should be of most interest to those of us working directly with animals!

Correlation vs causation

Replication

You're reading a study and it's got some very interesting, very convincing results. Exciting even. It can be very tempting to run out and start applying that new information and telling people that we now "know" X and it's been "proven." Scientists don't do this. Why not?

One study can support or not support a very specific hypothesis. It does not "prove" anything. It provides evidence. No one study will ever be able to examine every important factor that could be driving a behavior. Let's go back to our hypothetical play in the shelter dog study. Say the hypothesis was "if play reduces stress in shelter dogs, then shelter dogs that get played with will have lower stress hormone levels than those that don't get played with." Pretend that the study was conducted and the play group did indeed have lower stress hormone levels than the control group. This evidence provides *support* for the idea that playing with dogs in a shelter reduces their stress levels. However, it does not prove it—there are other possible explanations. Perhaps just getting them out of the cage and into a new environment is the determining factor. Maybe it's the increased interaction with people. Maybe it's the physical exercise. It could be a combination of factors.

This is why **replication** is important. Once a single study is completed, additional studies need to be conducted to start to work through the details. A second study could get at these questions by testing different things. Maybe the researchers pet the dogs and see if the stress still changes. Or they use a ball thrown by a machine with no one around to see how that impacts the results. Over time, and with many different studies approaching the question in slightly different ways, we start to get a more complete picture.

It's also possible that the results are just due to chance. Maybe the dogs who were randomly assigned to the play group were the ones that were better adjusted, and their stress levels would have gone down over the course of the study regardless.

In 2009, Dr. Craig Bennett presented a poster at the Human Brain Mapping Conference (2009). It generated a lot of buzz and is still talked about today. The official title was hefty; "Neural Correlates of Interspecies Perspective Taking in the Post-Mortem Atlantic Salmon:

An Argument for Proper Multiple Comparisons Correction." However, it's come to be known simply as "The Dead Salmon Study."

The researchers were examining brain activity related to perspective taking in a variety of subjects. One of the subjects was a dead salmon and, shockingly, the MRI indicated that it showed brain activity in response to a series of images depicting human social interactions!

How is this possible? That salmon was dead! What does this mean? To quote the researchers, "Either we have stumbled onto a rather amazing discovery in terms of post-mortem ichthyological cognition, or there is something a bit off with regard to our uncorrected statistical approach." (Bennett et al., 2009). Put in layman's terms, this means that of course there was no brain activity in the dead fish. Instead, it indicates that the statistical analysis used to identify brain activity produced a false positive—it indicated that brain activity was present, when it most definitely was *not*. In other words, the data was wrong. This is the reason replication is so important!

When research is done there is always a chance that the results are caused by something other than the factors being examined. If the results of a study are **significant** that simply means that the results are *most likely* the result of the specific variables in question. Put another way, statistically significant results are almost certainly actually relevant to the question you are trying to ask. Almost certainly is pretty vague, and scientists think so too, so they have gotten specific. In order for study results to be considered significant the likelihood that the results are just due to chance must be 5% or less. That is, we are at *least* 95% confident that the results we're seeing are actually due to the different factor(s) that are being examined.

Let's go back again to the hypothetical play with shelter dogs study. If the researchers find a significant difference between the dogs in the play group and the dogs in the non-play (control) group, that means we're at least 95% sure that the difference in stress is due to the play. However, there is still a 5% chance (or less) that those results happened for some other reason. As I mentioned earlier, it's possible the play group just happened to be a more relaxed group for some reason and their stress levels would have gone down anyway.

We want to make sure that the conclusions we draw are as accurate as possible. This is the second purpose of replication—to make sure that multiple studies find the same or very similar results. This allows us to be much more confident when we say "X causes Y" or "there is a relationship between X and Y," because while the results of a single study could simply be a fluke, the results of five, 10, 15 or more studies almost certainly are not.

Generalization

The next thing we must consider is generalization. Research studies occur under specific conditions. Even if something is true in one context, for one particular population, that does not necessarily mean it's true for other populations or in other contexts. It is important to be cautious about applying research results to different contexts or populations.

For example, can studies on rats be applied to dogs? Can studies on lab animals be applied to pets? This is a particularly important question when we are talking about things like stress because the vast majority of work in this area has been done on rodents. A smaller, but still substantial, number of studies have been done on humans. Comparatively little stress research has been done directly on dogs (with a bit of an exception for shelter dogs). The good news for the dog world is that there is a huge amount of agreement regarding stress and its impacts on the body across all mammals that have been studied—including humans, non-human primates, rodents and large carnivores. Therefore, chances are very high that what is true for rodents is also largely true for other mammals. There are bound to be some differences, but they are likely to be relatively minor. Czerwinski et al. (2016) argue that certain characteristics about rodents make them good models for stress-related behavior in dogs. Both have similar stress-related physiology, have litters with multiple offspring that are heavily dependent on maternal care and have similar developmental stages. We also know from multiple different studies, as outlined through the rest of this book, that evidence in dogs on the physiological and behavioral response to stress is in line with that done on other mammals.

We still need to pay attention to species-specific details, though. For example, the exact timing of a sensitive developmental period will vary from species to species based on that species' developmental timeline. Rats hit early adolescence when they are about five weeks old (Brenhouse and Andersen, 2011), so although early development is still important for them, by the time they are over five weeks, they have already moved out of the early development stage. In contrast, five-week-old puppies are still very much in the juvenile stage and are still in early development.

We also need to be very careful of making anecdotal observations of behavior and broadly applying that to entire groups. A particularly well-known example of this (at least in the professional dog world) is aggression and dominance. The initial view was that there was a link between dominance and aggression levels in wolves, with the more dominant animals being more aggressive. However, research on aggression and dominance in wolves and domestic dogs has shown that dominance hierarchies and their impact on behavior are quite complex. Too complex, in fact, to adequately cover here. There are a few key points to note, however.

First, researchers now believe that the role of dominance in wolves was initially overstated (Mech, 1999) and that most packs are organized as family groups. Second, the presence of a social hierarchy in wolves does not necessarily mean that domestic dogs establish social hierarchies. This is particularly true for pet dogs that are not likely to be competing for limited resources and are often surgically sterilized. So far, the research on the presence of dominance hierarchies in domestic dogs is mixed (see Bradshaw et al., 2009; and Schilder et al., 2014 for reviews). Furthermore, dominance and aggression are frequently unrelated (Cafazzo et al., 2010; Sands and Creelt, 2014). So even if pet dogs do establish dominance hierarchies, there is no evidence that all or even most aggression is linked to dominance. Dominance hierarchies (in all species that form them) are developed to control access to limited resources. In fact, they often function to *reduce* conflict and aggression. Therefore, dominance does not relate to certain types of aggression. Aggression toward strangers or growling or biting when feeling threatened would not fall under the category of "dominance aggression" even if such a thing exists. Indeed, we have good evidence that much aggressive behavior is correlated with fear and anxiety (Dinwoodie et al., 2019; Mikkola et al., 2021).

Despite this, there is a strong and persistent belief among many people that all aggression in dogs is a sign of dominance and that the way to address the so-called 'dominant behavior' is through confrontational and aggressive behavior of the owner toward the dog. There is absolutely no evidence to support this and, within the scientific literature, even researchers that believe there is evidence of dominance hierarchies in domestic dogs oppose the use of such hands on physically violent behavior toward dogs (Schilder et al., 2014). This is an excellent example of anecdotal evidence being **overgeneralized** to apply to pet dogs. (To their credit, I'm not sure this overgeneralization had anything to do with the scientists themselves. Although it certainly happens, scientists in general are *extremely* careful about overgeneralizing their results or overstating their findings. Unfortunately, the media isn't so cautious and often makes more out of a particular finding than the researchers themselves do.)

And finally, it's always important to remember that research findings are rarely absolute. Different individuals respond differently at different times. Genetics and individual differences play an important role. Please remember this: just because a study finds that X has a significant impact on Y, that doesn't mean you're going to see that impact every single time in every single animal.

Assessing scientific research

None of this means that science has no value. Far from it! Don't throw up your hands and give up, just be cautious when interpreting findings, particularly when it's just one study. Here are some things to keep in mind when reading a study:

- Was this a correlational or experimental study?
- How was the study designed? Was there a control group? Does the study design make sense? How many animals were used in the study?
- Were the results statistically significant? (Look for something called ***p* values**. They are too complicated to cover for this book, but they should be less than .05.)
- Who were the subjects of the study? How similar/dissimilar was this group to domestic dogs living in homes (or elsewhere, depending on what population of dogs you live and/or work with)? If they were not similar, is there reason to believe the results would generalize well (for example, the stress system of most mammals seems to be very similar).
- Do you agree with the researchers' conclusions? Are there other explanations that might make sense? What are they? What additional questions remain unanswered?

You may not always have access to the original scientific papers to read them in detail (though they are often available for free online). However, even if you don't have access to the original papers, these principles will help you do a better job of interpreting and applying the information you receive.

Keep the information in this appendix in mind as you apply the information in this book—and in all of the work that you do with dogs! It will make you better at what you do!

Cited Works

Agrawal, H.C. , Fox, M.W., Himwich, W.A. (1967). Neurochemical and behavioral effects of isolation-rearing in the dog, *Life Sciences*, Vol. 6, No. 1, pp. 71-78.

Alonso, S. J., Arevalo, R. et al. (1991). Effects of maternal stress during pregnancy on forced swimming test behavior of the offspring. *Physiology & Behavior*, Vol. 50, No. 3, pp. 511-517.

Alonso, S.J., Damas, C. et al. (2000). Behavioral despair in mice after prenatal stress. *Journal of Physiology and Biochemisty*, Vol. 56, pp. 77-82.

Akers, K.G., Yang, Z., DelVecchio, D.P. (2008). Social Competitiveness and Plasticity of Neuroendocrine Function in Old Age: Influence of Neonatal Novelty Exposure and Maternal Care Reliability. *PLoS ONE*, Vol. 3, No. 7, p. e2840.

American Psychiatric Association. (2013). Diagnostic and statistical manual of mental disorders (5th ed.). Washington, DC: Author.

Andersen, S.L., Teicher, M.H. (2008). Stress, sensitive periods and maturational events in adolescent depression. *Trends in Neuroscience*, Vol. 31, No. 4, pp. 183–19

Angle, C.T., Wakshlag, J.J., Gillette, R.L. et al. (2009). Hematologic, serum biochemical, and cortisol changes associated with anticipation of exercise and short duration high-intensity exercise in sled dogs. *Veterinary Clinical Pathology*, Vol. 38, No. 3, pp. 370-374.

Baas, J.M.P., van Ooijen, L., Goudriaan, A. et al. (2008). Failure to condition to a cue is associated with sustained contextual fear. *Acta Psychologica*, Vol. 127, No. 3, pp. 581-592.

Balleine, B.W. A., Dickinson A. (1998). The role of incentive learning in instrumental outcome revaluation by sensory-specific satiety. *Animal Learning & Behavior*, Vol. 26, pp. 46–59.

Bar-Haim, Y., Lamy, D., Pergamin, L. et al. (2007). Threat-related attentional bias in anxious and nonanxious individuals: a meta-analytic study. *Psychological Bulletin*, Vol. 133, No. 1, pp. 1-24.

Baratta, M.V., Christianson, J.P., Gomez, D.M. et al. (2007). Controllable versus uncontrollable stressors bi-directionally modulate conditioned but not innate fear. *Neuroscience*, Vol. 146, No. 4, pp. 1495–1503.

Barnard, S., Wells, D.L., Milligan, A.D.S. et al. (2018). Personality traits affecting judgement bias task performance in dogs (*Canis familiaris*). *Scientific Reports*, Vol. 8, 6660.

Bateson, M. and Matheson, S.M. (2007). Performance on a categorisation task suggests that removal of environmental enrichment induces 'pessimism' in captive European starlings (Sturnus vulgaris). *Animal Welfare*, Vol. 16, pp. 33-36.

Bath, K.G. (2020). Synthesizing Views to Understand Sex Differences in Response to Early Life Adversity. *Trends in Neuroscience*, Vol. 43, No. 5, pp. 300-310.

Beckner, V.E., Tucker, D.M., Delville, Y. et al. (2006). Stress facilitates consolidation of verbal memory for a film but does not affect retrieval. *Behavioral Neuroscience*, Vol. 120, No. 3, pp. 518–527.

Beerda, B., Schilder, M.B.H. et al. (1998). Behavioural, saliva cortisol and heart rate responses to different types of stimuli in dogs. *Applied Animal Behaviour Science*, Vol. 58, pp. 365-381.

Beerda, B., Schilder, M.B.H. et al. (1999). Chronic Stress in Dogs Subjected to Social and Spatial Restriction. I. Behavioral Responses. *Physiology & Behavior,* Vol. 66, No. 2, pp. 233-242.

Beerda, B., Schilder, M.B.H. et al. (2000). Behavioural and hormonal indicators of enduring environmental stress in dogs. *Animal Welfare*, Vol. 9, pp. 49-62.

Beery, A.K. and Kaufer, D. (2015). Stress, social behavior, and resilience: Insights from rodents. *Neurobiology of Stress*, Vol. 1, pp. 116-127.

Bell, A.M., Sih. A. (2007). Exposure to predation generates personality in three spinedsticklebacks. *Ecology Letters*, Vol. 10, No. 9, pp. 828–834.

Benaroya-Milshtein, N., Hollander, N., Apter, A. et al. (2004). Environmental enrichment in mice decreases anxiety, attenuates stress responses and enhances natural killer cell activity. *European Journal of Neuroscience*, Vol. 20, No. 5, pp. 1341-1347.

Bennett, C.M., Baird, A.A. (2009). Neural correlates of interspecies perspective taking in the post-mortem Atlantic Salmon: An argument for multiple comparisons correction. Prefrontal.org, http://prefrontal.org/files/posters/Bennett-Salmon-2009.pdf

Benoit, J.D., Rakic, P. et al. (2015). Prenatal stress induces spatial memory deficits and epigenetic changes in the hippocampus indicative of heterochromatin formation and reduced gene expression. *Behavioural Brain Research*, Vol. 281, pp. 1–8.

Beuving, G., Jones, R.B. and Blokhuis, HB. (1989). Adrenocortical and heterophil/ lymphocyte responses to challenge in hens showing short and long tonic immobility reactions. *British Poultry Science*, Vol. 30, No. 1, pp. 175–84.

Boissy, A. and Le Neindre, P. (1997). Behavioral, cardiac and cortisol responses to brief peer separation and reunion in cattle. *Physiology & Behavior*, Vol. 61, No. 5, pp. 693-699.

Boissy, A., Terlouw, C., Le Neindre, P. (1998). Presence of cues from stressed conspecifics increases reactivity to aversive events in cattle: evidence for the existence of alarm substances in urine. Physiology & Behavior, Vol. 63, No. 4, pp. 489–495.

Bosch, O.J., Nair, H.P., Ahern, T.H. et al. (2009). The CRF system mediates increased passive stress-coping behavior following the loss of a bonded partner in a monogamous rodent. *Neuropsychopharmacology*, Vol. 34, No. 6, pp. 1406-1415.

Bouton, M. (1993). Context, time, and memory retrieval in the interference of Pavlovian learning. *Psychological Bulletin,* Vol. 114, No. 1, pp. 80–99.

Bower, G.H. (1981). Mood and memory. *American Psychologist,* Vol. 36, No. 2, pp. 129-48.

Braastad, B.O., Osadchuk, L.V. et al. (1998). Effects of prenatal handling stress on adrenal weight and function and behaviour in novel situations in blue fox cubs (Alopex lagopus). *Applied Animal Behaviour Science,* Vol. 57, No. 1-2, pp. 157-169.

Bradshaw, J.W.S., Blackwell, E.J. et al. (2009). Dominance in domestic dogs — useful construct or bad habit ? *Journal of Veterinary Behavior,* Vol. 4, pp. 135-144.

Brachman, R.A., Lehmann, M.L., Maric, D. et al. (2015). Lymphocytes from chronically stressed mice confer antidepressant-like effects to naive mice. *The Journal of Neuroscience,* Vol. 35, No. 4, pp. 1530-1538.

Bradley, R. G., Binder, E.B., Epstein, M.P. et al. (2008). Influence of child abuse on adult depression: Moderation by the corticotropin-releasing hormone receptor gene. *Archives of General Psychiatry,* Vol. 65, No. 2, pp. 190–200.

Bray, E.E., Sammel, M.D., Cheney, D.L. et al. (2017). Effects of maternal investment, temperament, and cognition on guide dog success. *PNAS,* Vol. 114, No. 34, pp. 9128-9133.

Brenhouse, H.C. and Andersen, S.L. (2011). Developmental trajectories during adolescence in males and females: a cross-species understanding of underlying brain changes. *Neuroscience & Biobehavioral Reviews,* Vol. 35, No. 8, pp. 1687-1703.

Bruce, L.C., Heimberg, R.G. et al. (2012). Childhood maltreatment and social anxiety disorder: implications for symptom severity and response to pharmacotherapy. *Depression and Anxiety,* Vol. 29, No. 2, pp. 132–139.

Buchanan, T.W., Tranel, D., R. Adolphs, R. (2006). Impaired memory retrieval correlates with individual differences in cortisol response but not autonomic response. *Learning & Memory,* Vol. 13, No. 3, pp. 382–387.

Burke, A.R., McCormick, C.M. et al. (2017). Impact of adolescent social experiences on behavior and neural circuits implicated in mental illnesses. *Neuroscience and Biobehavioral Reviews*, Vol. 76, pp. 280-300.

Burman, O.H.P. and Mendl, M.T. (2018). A novel task to assess mood congruent memory bias in non-human animals. *Journal of Neuroscience Methods*, Vol. 308, pp. 269-275,

Buss, C., Davis, E.P., Muftuler, L.T. et al. (2010). High pregnancy anxiety during mid-gestation is associated with decreased gray matter density in 6–9-year-old children. *Psychoneuroendocrinology,* Vol. 35, No. 1, pp. 141–153.

Buss, C., Lord, C., Wadiwalla, M. et al. (2007). Maternal care modulates the relationship between prenatal risk and hippocampal volume in women but not in men. *The Journal of Neuroscience*, Vol. 27, No. 10, pp. 2592–2595.

Phillips Buttner, A., Thompson, B., Stresser, R. et al. (2015). Evidence for a synchronization of hormonal states between humans and dogs during competition. *Physiology & Behavior*, Vol. 147, pp. 54-62.

Cafazzo, S., Valsecchi, P., Bonanni, R. et al. (2010). Dominance in relation to age, sex, and competitive contexts in a group of free-ranging domestic dogs, *Behavioral Ecology*, Vol. 21, No. 3, pp. 443–455.

Cahill, L., Babinsky, R., Markowitsch, H.J. et al. (1995). The amygdala and emotional memory. *Nature,* Vol. 377, No. 6547, pp. 295–296.

Cahill, L. and McGaugh, J.L. (1995). A novel demonstration of enhanced memory associated with emotional arousal. *Consciousness and Cognition*, Vol. 4, No. 4, pp. 410-421.

Caldji, C., Diorio, J., Meaney, M.J. (2000). Variations in maternal care in infancy regulate the development of stress reactivity. *Biological Psychiatry*, Vol. 48, pp. 1164–1174.

Caldji, C., Tannenbaum, B., Sharma, S., et al. (1998). Maternal care during infancy regulates the development of neural systems mediating the expression of fearfulness in the rat. *PNAS*, Vol. 95, pp. 5335–5340.

Cannas, S., Frank, D., Minero, M. et al. (2014). Video analysis of dogs suffering from anxiety when left home alone and treated with clomipramine. *Journal of Veterinary Behavior,* Vol. 9, No. 2, pp. 50-57.

Caspi, A., Sugden, K., Moffitt, T.E. (2003). Influence of life stress on depression: Moderation a polymorphism in the 5-HTT gene. *Science,* Vol. 301, No. 2003, pp. 386-389.

Champagne, D.L., Bagot, R.C., van Hasselt, F. et al. (2008). Maternal Care and Hippocampal Plasticity: Evidence for Experience-Dependent Structural Plasticity, Altered Synaptic Functioning, and Differential Responsiveness to Glucocorticoids and Stress. *Journal of Neuroscience*, Vol. 28, No. 23, pp. 6037-6045.

Chmelíková, E., Bolechová, P., Chaloupková, I. et al. (2020). Salivary cortisol as a marker of acute stress in dogs: a review. *Domestic Animal Endocrinology*, Vol. 72, 106428.

Christianson, J.P., Paul, E.D., Irani, M. et al. (2008). The role of prior stressor controllability and the dorsal raphé nucleus in sucrose preference and social exploration. *Behavioural Brain Research*, Vol. 193, No. 1, pp. 87-93.

Clark, F.E. (2011). Great ape cognition and captive care: Can cognitive challenges enhance well-being? *Applied Animal Behaviour Science*, Vol. 102, No. 3-4, pp. 246-261.

Clark, S.D., Martin, F., McGowan, R.T.S. et al. (2020). Physiological State of Therapy Dogs during Animal-Assisted Activities in an Outpatient Setting. *Animals*, Vol. 10, No. 5, p. 819.

Clarke, A.S., and Schneider, M.L. (1993). Prenatal stress has long-term effects on behavioral responses to stress in juvenile rhesus monkeys. *Developmental Psychobiology*, Vol. 25, No. 5, pp. 293-304.

Collins, A., Hill, L.E., Chandramohan, Y. et al. (2009). Exercise improves cognitive responses to psychological stress through enhancement of epigenetic mechanisms and gene expression in the dentate gyrus. *PloS One*, Vol. 4, No. 1, e4330.

Coe, C.L., Glass, J.C., Wiener, S.G. et al. (1983). Behavioral, but not physiological adaptation to repeated separation in mother and infant primates. *Psychoneuroendocrinology,* Vol. 8, No. 4, pp. 401–409.

Conger, J.J., Sawrey, W.L., and Turrell, E.S. (1958). The role of social experience in the production of gastric ulcers in hooded rats placed in a conflict situation. *The Journal of Abnormal and Social Psychology*, Vol. 57, No. 2, pp. 214–220.

Conrad, C.D. (2008). Chronic stress-induced hippocampal vulnerability: the glucocorticoid vulnerability hypothesis. *Reviews in the Neurosciences*, Vol. 19. No. 6, pp. 395–411.

Cooper, J.J., Cracknell, N., Hardiman, J. et al. (2014). The Welfare Consequences and Efficacy of Training Pet Dogs with Remote Electronic Training Collars in Comparison to Reward Based Training. *PLoS ONE*, Vol. 9, No. 10, e110931.

Coppola, C.L., Grandin, T., Enns, R.M. (2006). Human interaction and cortisol: can human contact reduce stress for shelter dogs? *Physiology & Behavior*, Vol. 87, No. 3, pp. 537-541.

Cordero, M.I., Venero, C., Kruyt, N.D. et al. (2003). Prior exposure to a single stress session facilitates subsequent contextual fear conditioning in rats: Evidence for a role of corticosterone. *Hormones and Behavior*, Vol. 44, pp. 338-345.

Corsetti, S., Borruso, S., Di Traglia, M. et. al. (2018). Bold personality makes domestic dogs entering a shelter less vulnerable to disease. *PLoS One,* Vol. 13, No. 3, e0193794.

Coulton, L.E., Waran, N.K., Young, R.J. (1997). Effects of foraging enrichment on the behaviour of parrots. *Animal Welfare*, Vol. 6, No. 4, pp. 357-363.

Cratty, M.S., Ward, H.E., Johnson, E.A. et al. (1995). Prenatal stress increases corticotropin-releasing factor (CRF) content and release in rat amygdala minces. *Brain Research*, Vol. 675, No. 1-2, pp. 297-302.

Cruz-Pereira, J. S., Rea, K. et al. (2020). Depression's Unholy Trinity: Dysregulated stress, immunity, and the microbiome. *Annual Review of Psychology,* Vol. 71, pp. 49-78.

Cui, M., Yang, Y., Yang, J. et al. (2006). Enriched environment experience overcomes the memory deficits and depressive-like behavior induced by early life stress. *Neuroscience Letters*, Vol. 404, No. 1-2, pp. 208-212.

Czerwinski, V. H., Smith, B.P. et al. (2016). The influence of maternal care on stress-related behaviors in domestic dogs: What can we learn from the rodent literature? *Journal of Veterinary Behavior*, Vol. 14, pp. 52-59.

Dalle Molle, R., Portella, A.K., Goldani, M.Z. et al. (2012). Associations between parenting behavior and anxiety in a rodent model and a clinical sample: relationship to peripheral BDNF levels. *Translational Psychiatry*, Vol. 2, e195.

Darwish, D., Esquivel, G.B., Houtz, J.C. et al. (2001). Play and social skills in maltreated and non-maltreated preschoolers during peer interactions. *Child Abuse and Neglect*, Vol. 25, No. 1, pp. 13–31.

Daskalakis, N., Rijal, C.M., King, C. et al. (2018). Recent genetics and epigenetics approaches to PTSD. *Current Psychiatry Reports*, Vol. 20, 30.

Davitz, J.R. and Mason, D.J.M. (1955). Socially facilitated reduction of a fear response in rats. *Journal of Comparative and Physiological Psychology*, Vol. 48, No. 3, pp. 149–151.

de Carvalho, I.R., Nunes, T., de Sousa, L. et al. (2020). The combined use of salivary cortisol concentrations, heart rate, and respiratory rate for the welfare assessment of dogs involved in AAI programs. *Journal of Veterinary Behavior*, Vol. 36, pp. 26-33.

de Castro, A.C.V., Fuchs, D., Morello, G.M. et al. (2020). Does training method matter? Evidence for the negative impact of aversive-based methods on companion dog welfare. PLoS One, Vol. 15, No. 12, e0225023.

de Kloet, E.R. (1991). Brain corticosteroid receptor balance and homeostatic control. *Frontiers in Neuroendocrinology*, Vol. 12, No. 2, pp. 95–164.

de Quervain, D., Schwabe, L., Roozendaal, B. (2017). Stress, glucocorticoids and memory: implications for treating fear-related disorders. *Nature Reviews Neuroscience*, Vol. 18, No. 1, pp. 7-19.

de Souza, M.A., Centenaro, L.A. et al. (2013). Prenatal stress produces social behavior deficits and alters the number of oxytocin and vasopressin neurons in adult rats. *Neurochemical Research*, Vol. 38, No. 7, pp. 1479–1489.

Deslauriers, J., Toth, M., Der-Avakian, A. et al. (2018). Current status of animal models of PTSD: behavioral and biological phenotypes, and future challenges in improving translation. *Biological Psychiatry*, Vol. 83, No. 10, pp. 895-907.

Dias, B.G. and Ressler, K.J. (2014). Parental olfactory experience influences behavior and neural structure in subsequent generations. *Nature Neuroscience*, Vol. 17, pp. 89-96.

Dickinson, A. (1985). Actions and habits: the development of behavioral autonomy. *Philosophical Transactions of the Royal Society B*, Vol. 308, No. 1135, pp. 67–78.

Dingemanse, N.J., Thomas, D.K., Wright, J., et al. (2007). Behavioural syndromes differ predictably between twelve populations of three-spined stickleback. *The Journal of Animal Ecology*, Vol. 76, No. 6, pp. 1128–1138.

Dinwoodie, I.R., Dwyer, B., Zottola, V. et al. (2019). Demographics and comorbidity of behavior problems in dogs. *Journal of Veterinary Behavior*, Vol. 32, pp. 62-71.

Dinwoodie, I.R., Zottola, V., Dodman, N.H. (2021). An investigation into the effectiveness of various professionals and behavior modification programs, with or without medication, for the treatment of canine aggression. *Journal of Veterinary Behavior*, Vol. 43, pp. 46-53.

Diverio, S., Barbato, O., Cavallina, R. et al. (2016). A simulated avalanche search and rescue mission induces temporary physiological and behavioural changes in military dogs. *Physiology & Behavior*, Vol. 163, pp. 193-202.

Douglas, C., Bateson, M., Walsh, C. et al. (2012). Environmental enrichment induces optimistic cognitive biases in pigs. *Applied Animal Behaviour Science*, Vol. 139.

Douglas, L.A., Varlinskaya, E.I., Spear, L.P. (2004). Rewarding properties of social interactions in adolescent and adult male and female rats: impact of social versus isolate housing of subjects and partners. *Developmental Psychobiology*, Vol. 45, No. 3, pp.153–162.

Dreschel, N.A. (2010). The effects of fear and anxiety on health and lifespan in pet dogs. *Applied Animal Behaviour Science*, Vol. 125, No. 3-4, pp. 157-162.

Duman, R.S., Deyama, S., Fogaça. M.V. (2019). Role of BDNF in the pathophysiology and treatment of depression: Activity-dependent effects distinguish rapid-acting antidepressants. *European Journal of Neuroscience*, Vol. 53, pp. 126-139.

Duncan, L.E., Cooper, B.N., Shen, H. (2018). Robust findings from 25 years of PTSD genetics research. Current Psychiatry Reports. Vol. 20, p. 115.

Duranton, C. and Horowitz, A. (2019). Let me sniff! Nosework induces positive judgment bias in pet dogs. *Applied Animal Behaviour Science*, Vol. 211, pp. 61-66.

Einon, D.F., Morgan, M.J. (1977). A critical period for social isolation in the rat. *Developmental Psychobiology*, Vol. 10, No. 2, pp. 123–132.

Einon, D.F., Morgan, M.J., Kibbler, C.C. (1978). Brief periods of socialization and later behavior in the rat. *Developmental Psychobiology*, Vol. 11, No. 3, pp. 213–225.

Eisenberger, R. (1992). Learned industriousness. *Psychological Review*, Vol. 99, No. 2, pp. 248-267.

Ellis, B.J. and Boyce, W.T. (2008). Biological Sensitivity to Context. *Current Directions in Psychological Science*, Vol. 17, No. 3, pp. 183-187.

Elzinga, B.M., Bakker, A., Bremner, J.D. (2005). Stress-induced cortisol elevations are associated with impaired delayed, but not immediate recall. *Psychiatry Research*, Vol.134, No. 3, pp. 211–223.

Entringer, S., Kumsta, R. et al. (2008a). Influence of prenatal psychosocial stress on cytokine production in adult women. *Developmental Psychobiology*, Vol. 50, No. 6, pp. 579–587.

Entringer, S., Wüst, S. et al. (2008b). Prenatal psychosocial stress exposure is associated with insulin resistance in young adults. *American Journal of Obstetrics and Gynecology*, Vol. 199, No. 5, pp. 498.e1-7.

Ernst, K., Tuchscherer, M., Kanitz, E., et al. (2006). Effects of attention and rewarded activity on immune parameters and wound healing in pigs. *Physiology & Behavior*, Vol. 89, No. 3, pp. 448-456.

Evans, G.W. and English, K. (2002). The Environment of Poverty: Multiple Stressor Exposure, Psychophysiological Stress, and

Socioemotional Adjustment. *Child Development*, Vol. 73, No. 4, pp. 1238-1248.

Eyck, H.J.F., Buchanan, K.L., Crino, O.L. et al. (2019). Effects of developmental stress on animal phenotype and performance: a quantitative review. *Biological Reviews*, Vol. 94, No. 3, pp. 1143-1160.

Eysenck, M.W., Mogg, K., May, J. et al. (1991). Bias in interpretation of ambiguous sentences related to threat in anxiety. *Journal of Abnormal Psychology*, Vol. 100, No. 2, pp. 144–150.

Fenoglio, K.A., Brunson, K.L., Baram, T.Z. (2006). Hippocampal neuroplasticity induced early-life stress: Functional and molecular aspects. *Frontiers in Neuroendocrinology*, Vol. 27, No. 2, pp. 180-192.

Fenster, R.J., Lebois, L.A.M., Ressler, K.J. et al. (2018). Brain circuit dysfunction in post-traumatic stress disorder: from mouse to man. *Nature Reviews Neuroscience*, Vol. 19, No. 9, pp. 535-551.

Fernandes, G.J., Olsson, I.A.S., de Castro. A.C.V. (2017). Do aversive-based training methods actually compromise dog welfare?: A literature review. *Applied Animal Behaviour Science*, Vol. 196, pp. 1-12.

Fernandez-Teruel, A., Gimenez-Lort, L., Escorihuela, R.M. et al. (2002). Early-life handling stimulation and environmental enrichment: are some of their effects mediated by similar neural mechanisms? Pharmacology, Biochemistry and Behavior, Vol. 73, pp. 233–245.

Ferrari, F. and Villa, R.F. (2017). The neurobiology of depression: An integrated overview from biological theories to clinical evidence. *Molecular Neurobiology*, Vol. 54, No. 7, pp. 4847–4865.

Finley, J.C. Jr., O'Leary, M., Wester D. et al. (2004). A genetic polymorphism of the alpha2-adrenergic receptor increases autonomic responses to stress. *Journal of Applied Physiology*, Vol. 96, No. 6, pp. 2231–2239.

Fokkema, D.S., Koolhaas, J.M., van der Gugten, J. (1995). Individual characteristics of behavior, blood pressure, and adrenal hormones in colony rats. *Physiology and Behavior.* Vol. 57, No. 5, 857e862.

Fokkema, D.S., Smit, K., van der Gugten, J. et al. (1988). A coherent pattern among social behavior, blood pressure, corticosterone and catecholamine measures in individual male rats. *Physiology & Behavior*, Vol. 42, No. 5, pp. 485-489.

Fontaine, K.R., Manstead, A.S.R., Wagner, H. (1993). Optimism, perceived control over stress, and coping. *European Journal of Personality*, Vol. 7, No. 4, pp. 267-281.

Francis, D., Diorio, J., Liu, D. et al. (1999). Nongenomic Transmission Across Generations of Maternal Behavior and Stress Responses in the Rat. *Science*, Vol. 286, No. 5442, pp. 1155-1158.

Francis, D.D., Diorio, J., Plotsky, P.M. et al. (2002). Environmental enrichment reverses the effects of maternal separation on stress reactivity, *The Journal of Neuroscience*, Vol. 22, No. 18, pp. 7840–7843.

Fraser, A.F., and Broom, D.M. (1990). Farm Animal Behavior and Welfare, 3rd ed. Bailliere Tindall, London, UK.

Fox, M.W. and Stelzner, D. (1967). The effects of early experience on the development of inter and intraspecies social relationships in the dog. *Animal Behaviour*, Vol. 15, pp. 377-386.

Foyer, P., Wilsson, E., Jensen, P. (2016). Levels of maternal care in dogs affect adult offspring temperament. *Scientific Reports*, Vol. 6, 19253.

Foyer, P., Wilsson, E., Wright, D. et al. (2013). Early experiences modulate stress coping in a population of German shepherd dogs. *Applied Animal Behaviour Science*, Vol. 146, No. 1-4, pp. 79-87.

Girotti, M., Pac, T.W.W., Gaylord, R.I. et al. (2006). Habituation to repeated restraint stress is associated with lack of stress-induced c-fos expression in primary sensory processing areas of the rat brain. *Neuroscience*, Vol. 138, No. 4, pp. 1067-1081.

Giubilei, F., Patacchioli, F.R., Antonini, G. et al. (2001). Altered circadian cortisol secretion in Alzheimer's disease: Clinical and neuroradiological aspects. *Journal of Neuroscience Research*, Vol. 66, No. 2, pp. 262-265.

Glaser, R. and Kiecolt-Glaser, J.K. (2005). Stress-induced immune dysfunction: Implications for health. *Nature Reviews Immunology*, Vol. 5, pp. 243-251.

Glasper, E.R. and DeVries, A.C. (2005). Social structure influences effects of pair housing on wound healing. *Brain Behavior and Immunity*, Vol. 19, No. 1, pp. 61–68.

Glenk, L.M. (2017). Current perspectives on therapy dog welfare in animal-assisted interventions. *Animals*, Vol. 7, No. 2.

Glenk, L.M., Kothgassner, O.D., Stetina, B.U. et al. (2014). Salivary cortisol and behavior in therapy dogs during animal-assisted interventions: A pilot study. *Journal of Veterinary Behavior*, Vol. 9, pp. 98-106.

Gluck, J.P. and Sackett, G.P. (1976). Extinction deficits in socially isolated rhesus monkeys (*Macaca mulatta*). *Developmental Psychology, Vol. 12,* No. 2, pp. 173–174.

Gluckman, P.D., Hanson, M.A., Beedle A.S. (2007). Early life events and their consequences for later disease: A life history and evolutionary perspective. *American Journal of Human Biology*, Vol. 19, pp. 1-19.

Goldman, L., Winget, C., Hollingshead, G.W. et al. (1973). Postweaning development of negative feedback in the pituitary-adrenal system of the rat. *Neuroendocrinology*, Vol. 12, pp. 199-211.

Goodkin, F. (1976). Rats learn the relationship between responding and environmental events: An expansion of the learned helplessness hypothesis. *Learning and Motivation*, Vol. 7, No. 3, pp. 382-393.

Gottschalk, M.G. and Domschke, K. (2017). Genetics of generalized anxiety disorder and related traits. *Dialogues in clinical neuroscience*, Vol. 19, No. 2, pp. 59-168.

Gourkow, N. and C.J.C. Phillips. (2016). Effect of cognitive enrichment on behavior, mucosal immunity and upper respiratory disease of shelter cats rated as frustrated on arrival. *Preventative Veterinary Medicine*, Vol. 131, pp. 103-110.

Green, M.K., Joshi, R.A. et al. (2011). Prenatal Stress Induces Long Term Stress Vulnerability, Compromising Stress Response Systems in the Brain and Impairing Extinction of Conditioned Fear after Adult Stress. *Neuroscience*, Vol. 192, pp. 438–451.

Grupe, D. and Nitschke, J. (2013). Uncertainty and anticipation in anxiety: an integrated neurobiological and psychological perspective. *Nature Reviews, Neuroscience*, Vol. 14, No. 7, pp. 488–501.

Guan, L., Jia, N. et al. (2013). The involvement of erk/creb/bcl-2 in depression-like behavior in prenatally stressed offspring rats. *Brain Research Bulletin*, Vol. 99, pp. 1–8.

Guardini, G., Mariti, C., Bowen, J. et al. (2016). Influence of morning maternal care on the behavioural responses of 8-week-old Beagle puppies to new environmental and social stimuli. *Applied Animal Behaviour Science*, Vol. 181, pp. 137-144.

Guardini, G., Bowen, J., Mariti, C. et al. (2017). Influence of Maternal Care on Behavioural Development of Domestic Dogs (Canis Familiaris) Living in a Home Environment. *Animals*, Vol. 7, No. 12.

Gunnar, M.R. and Donzella, B. (2002). Social regulation of the cortisol levels in early human development. *Psychoneuroendocrinology*, Vol. 27, pp. 199-220.

Gunnar, M.R., Frenn, K., Wewerka, S.S. et al. (2009). Moderate versus severe early life stress: associations with stress reactivity and regulation in 10-12-year-old children. *Psychoneuroendocrinology*, Vol. 34, No. 1, pp. 62–75.

Hagen, K. and Broom, D.M. (2004). Emotional reactions to learning in cattle. *Applied Animal Behaviour Science*, Vol. 85, pp. 203–213.

Halligan, S.L., Herbert, J., Goodyer, I. et al. (2007). Disturbances in Morning Cortisol Secretion in Association with Maternal Postnatal Depression Predict Subsequent Depressive Symptomatology in Adolescents. *Biological Psychiatry*, Vol. 62, No. 1, pp. 40-46.

Harding, E., Paul, E., Mendl, M. (2004). Cognitive bias and affective state. *Nature*, Vol. 427, p. 312.

Hare, B. and M. Tomasello. (2005). Human-like social skills in dogs? *Trends in Cognitive Sciences*, Vol. 9, No. 9, pp. 439-444.

Harlow, H.F. (1950). Learning and satiation of responses in intrinsically motivated complex puzzle performance by monkeys.

Journal of Comparative and Physiological Psychology, Vol. 43, No. 4, pp. 289–294.

Harlow, H.F., Dodsworth, R.O., Harlow, M.K. (1965). Total social isolation in monkeys. *PNAS*, Vol. 54, pp. 90-97.

Hartley, C.A., Gorun, A., Reddan, M.C. et al. (2014). Stressor controllability modulates fear extinction in humans. *Neurobiology of Learning and Memory*, Vol. 113, pp. 149–156.

Hefner, K., and Holmes, A. (2007). Ontogeny of fear-, anxiety- and depression-related behavior across adolescence in C57BL/6 J mice. Behavioural Brain Research, Vol. 176, No. 2, pp. 210–215.

Heim, C., Newport, D.J. et al. (2000). Pituitary-adrenal and autonomic responses to stress in women after sexual and physical abuse in childhood. *JAMA*, Vol. 284, No. 5, Aug. pp. 592–97.

Held, S. (2017). Play Behaviour. In P. Jensen (Ed.), *The Ethology of domestic animals: An introductory text* (pp. 90-103). CABI.

Hennessy, M.B. (2013). Using hypothalamic–pituitary–adrenal measures for assessing and reducing the stress of dogs in shelters: A review. *Applied Animal Behaviour Science*, Vol. 149, pp. 1-12.

Hennessy, M.B., Davis, H.N., Williams, M.T. (1997). Plasma Cortisol Levels of Dogs at a County Animal Shelter. *Physiology & Behavior*, Vol. 62, No. 3, pp. 485-490.

Hennessy, M.B., Voith, V.L., Mazzei, S.J. et al. (2001). Behavior and cortisol levels of dogs in a public animal shelter, and an exploration of the ability of these measures to predict problem behavior after adoption. *Applied Animal Behaviour Science*, Vol. 73, No. 3, pp. 217-233.

Hennessy, M.B. and Weinberg, J. (1990). Adrenocortical activity during conditions of brief social separation in preweaning rats. *Behavioral & Neural Biology*, Vol. 54, pp. 42-55.

Hennessy, M.B., Willen, R.M., Schiml, P.A. (2020). Psychological Stress, Its Reduction, and Long-Term Consequences: What Studies with Laboratory Animals Might Teach Us about Life in the Dog Shelter. *Animals*, Vol. 10, No. 11, p. 2061.

Hiby, E.F., Rooney, N.J., Bradshaw, J.W.S. (2006). Behavioural and physiological responses of dogs entering re-homing kennels. *Physiology & Behavior*, Vol. 89, pp. 385-391.

Hocking, D.P., Salverson, M., Evans, A.R. (2015). Foraging-Based Enrichment Promotes More Varied Behaviour in Captive Australian Fur Seals (Arctocephalus pusillus doriferus). *PLoS ONE*, Vol. 10, No. 5, e0124615.

Hofer, M.A. (1994). Early social relationship as regulators of infant physiology and behavior. *Acta Paediatrica (Supplement)*, Vol. 397, pp. 9-18.

Höglin, A., Van Poucke, E., Katajamaa, R. et al. (2021). Long-term stress in dogs is related to the human-dog relationship and personality traits. *Scientific Reports*, Vol. 11, No. 1, p. 8612.

Hol, T., Van den Berg, C.L., Van Ree, J.M. (1999). Isolation during the play period in infancy decreases adult social interactions in rats. *Behavioral Brain Research*, Vol. 100, No. 1-2, pp. 91–97.

Horváth, Z., Igyárto, B., Magyar, A. et al. (2007). Three different coping styles in police dogs exposed to a short-term challenge. *Hormones and Behavior*, Vol. 52, pp. 621-630.

Hu, C., Luo, Y., Wang, H. et al. (2017). Re-evaluation of the interrelationships among the behavioral tests in rats exposed to chronic unpredictable mild stress. *PLoS ONE*, Vol. 12, No. 9, e0185129.

Hueston, C.M., Cryan, J.F., Nolan, Y.M. (2017). Stress and adolescent hippocampal neurogenesis: diet and exercise as cognitive modulators, Translational Psychiatry, 7, p. 1-17.

Huntingford, F.A. (1982). Do inter- and intraspecific aggression vary in relation to predation pressure in sticklebacks? *Animal Behaviour*, Vol. 30, No. 3, pp. 909–916.

Huot, R.L., Gonzalez, C.O., Ladd, K.V. et al. (2004). Foster litters prevent hypothalamic-pituitary adrenal axis sensitization mediated by neonatal maternal separation. *Psychoneuroendocrinology*, Vol. 29, pp. 279-289.

Huot, R.L., Smith, M.A. et al. (1997). Alterations of maternal-infant interaction as a result of maternal separation in Long Evans rats and its behavioral and neuroendocrine consequences. *Psychoneuroendocrinology*, Vol. 22 (Supplement 2), S173.

Huot, R.L., Thrivikraman, K., Meaney, M.J. et al. (2001). Development of adult ethanol preference and anxiety as a consequence of neonatal maternal separation in Long Evans rats and reversal with antidepressant treatment. *Psychopharmacology*, Vol. 158. pp. 366-373.

Inglis, I.R., Forkman, B., Lazarus, J. (1997). Free food or earned food? A review and fuzzy model of contra freeloading. *Animal Behaviour*, Vol. 53, No. 6, pp. 1171-1191.

Isgor, C., Kabbaj, M., Akil, H. et al. (2004). Delayed effects of chronic variable stress during peripubertal-juvenile period on hippocampal morphology and on cognitive and stress axis functions in rats. *Hippocampus*, Vol. 14, No. 5, pp. 636-648.

Ishikawa, S., Saito, Y., Yanagawa, Y. et al. (2012). Early postnatal stress alters extracellular signal-regulated kinase signaling in the corticolimbic system modulating emotional circuitry in adult rats. *European Journal of Neuroscience*, Vol. 35, No. 1, pp. 135–145.

Issa, A.M., Rowe, W., Gauthier, S. et al. (1990). Hypothalamic-pituitary-adrenal activity in aged, cognitively impaired and cognitively unimpaired rats. *The Journal of Neuroscience*, Vol. 10, No. 10, pp. 3247-3254.

Izquierdo, A., Wellman, C.L., Holmes, A. (2006). Brief uncontrollable stress causes dendritic retraction in infra limbic cortex and resistance to fear extinction in mice. *Journal of Neuroscience*, Vol. 26, No. 21, pp. 5733–5738.

Joëls, M., Pu, Z., Wiegert, O. et al. (2006). Learning under stress: how does it work? *Trends in Cognitive Science*, Vol. 10, No. 4, pp. 152–158.

Joffe, J.M., Rawson, R., Mulick, J.A. (1973). Control of their environment reduces emotionality in rats. *Science*, Vol. 180, No. 4093, pp. 1383-1384.

Jones, A.C. and Josephs, R.A. (2006). Interspecies hormonal interactions between man and the domestic dog (Canis familiaris). *Hormones and Behavior*, Vol. 50, No. 3, pp. 393-400.

Judo, C., Matsumoto, M., Yamazaki, D. et. al. (2010). Early stress exposure impairs synaptic potentiation in the rat medial prefrontal cortex underlying contextual fear extinction. *Neuroscience*, Vol 169, No. 4, pp. 1705–1714.

Juster, R., McEwen, B.S. et al. (2010). Allostatic load biomarkers of chronic stress and impact on health and cognition. *Neuroscience and Biobehavioral Reviews,* Vol. 35, pp. 2-16.

Kalinichev, M. et al. (2002). Long-lasting changes in stress-induced corticosterone response and anxiety-like behaviors as a consequence of neonatal maternal separation in Long–Evans rats. *Pharmacology, Biochemistry and Behavior,* Vol. 73, pp. 131-140.

Kapoor, A. and Matthews, S.G. (2005). Short periods of prenatal stress affect growth, behaviour and hypothalamo-pituitary-adrenal axis activity in male guinea pig offspring. *The Journal of Physiology*, Vol. 566, pp. 967–977.

Karlamangla, A.S., Singer, B.H. et al. (2006). Reduction in allostatic load in older adults is associated with lower all-cause mortality risk: MacArthur studies of successful aging. *Psychosomatic medicine*, Vol. 68, pp. 500-507.

Kendig, M.D., Bowen, M.T., Kemp, A.H. et al. (2011). Predatory threat induces huddling in adolescent rats and residual changes in early adulthood suggestive of increased resilience. *Behavioural Brain Research*, Vol. 225, No. 2, pp. 405-414.

Keshet, G. I., and Weinstock, M. (1995). Maternal naltrexone prevents morphological and behavioral alterations induced in rats by prenatal stress. *Pharmacology Biochemistry and Behavior*, Vol. 50, No. 3, pp. 413–419.

Khoshaba, D.M., and Maddi, S.R. (1999). Early experiences in hardiness development. *Consulting Psychology Journal: Practice and Research*, Vol. 51, No. 2, pp. 106–116.

Kiddie, J. and Collins, L. (2015). Identifying environmental and management factors that may be associated with the quality of life of kennelled dogs (Canis familiaris). *Applied Animal Behaviour Science*, Vol. 167, pp. 43-55.

Kiecolt-Glaser, J.K., Marucha, P.T. et al. (1995). Slowing of wound healing by psychological stress. *Lancet*, Vol. 346, pp. 1194-1196.

Kikusui, T., Winslow, J. T., Mori, Y. (2006). Social buffering: relief from stress and anxiety. *Philosophical transactions of the Royal Society of London. Series B, Biological sciences*, Vol. 361, No. 1476, pp. 2215–2228.

King, C., Watter, J. and Mungre. S. (2011). Effect of a time-out session with working animal-assisted therapy dogs. *Journal of Veterinary Behavior Clinical Applications and Research*, Vol. 6, No. 4, pp. 232-238.

Kinsley, C., and Svare, B. (1986). Prenatal stress reduces intermale aggression in mice. *Physiology & Behavior*, Vol. 36, No. 4, pp. 783–786.

Kiyokawa, Y., Kikusui, T., Takeuchi, Y. et al. (2004). Partner's stress status influences social buffering effects in rats. *Behavioral Neuroscience*, Vol. 118, No. 4, pp. 798-804.

Klaassen, T., Riedel, W.J., Deutz, N.E.P. (2002). Mood congruent memory bias induced by tryptophan depletion. *Psychological Medicine*, Vol. 32, No. 1, pp.167-172.

Klein, D.C., Fencil-Morse, E., Seligman. M.E.P. (1976). Learned helplessness, depression, and the attribution of failure. *Journal of Personality and Social Psychology*. Vol. 33, No. 5, pp. 508–516.

Knox, D., George, S.A., Fitzpatrick, C.J. et al. (2012). Single prolonged stress disrupts retention of extinguished fear in rats. *Learning & Memory*, Vol. 19, No. 2, pp. 43–49.

Koehl, M., Darnaudéry, D., Dulluc, J. et al. (1999). Prenatal stress alters circadian activity of hypothalamo–pituitary–adrenal axis and hippocampal corticosteroid receptors in adult rats of both gender. *Journal of Neurobiology*, Vol. 40, No. 3, pp. 302-315.

Koolhaas, J.M., Korte, S.M., De Boer, S.F. et al. (1999). Coping styles in animals: current status in behavior and stress-physiology. *Neuroscience and Biobehavioral Reviews*, Vol. 23, pp. 925-935.

Koolhaas, J.M. and Van Reenen, C.G. (2016). Animal behavior and well-being symposium: Interaction between coping style/personality, stress, and welfare: relevance for domestic farm animals. *Journal of Animal Science*, Vol. 94, pp. 2284-2296.

Korte, S.M., Buwalda, B., Gouws, G.A. et al. (1992). Conditioned neuroendocrine and cardiovascular stress responsiveness accompanying behavioral passivity and activity in aged and in young rats. *Physiology & Behavior*, Vol. 51, No. 4, 815e822.

Korte, S.M., Koolhaas, J.M. et al. (2005). The Darwinian concept of stress: benefits of allostasis and costs of allostatic load and the trade-offs in health and disease. *Neuroscience & Biobehavioral Reviews*, Vol. 29, No. 1, pp. 3-38.

Kruger, K.A. and Serpell, J.A. (2006). Animal-assisted interventions in mental health: Definitions and theoretical foundations. In A. H. Fine (Ed.), Handbook on animal-assisted therapy: Theoretical foundations and guidelines for practice (pp. 21–38). Academic Press.

Kwapis, J.L. and Wood, M.A. (2014). Epigenetic mechanisms in fear conditioning: implications for treating post-traumatic stress disorder. *Trends in Neurosciences*, Vol. 37, No. 12, pp. 706-720.

Landfield, P.W., Baskin, R.K. and Pitler, T.A. (1981). Brain aging correlates: retardation by hormonal-pharmacological treatments. *Science*, Vol. 214, No. 4520, pp. 581-584.

Landfield, P.W., Blalock, E.M., Chen, K.C. et al. (2007). A New Glucocorticoid Hypothesis of Brain Aging: Implications for Alzheimer's Disease. *Current Alzheimer Research*, Vol. 4, No. 2, pp. 205-212.

Landfield, P.W., Waymire, J.C., Lynch, G. (1978). Hippocampal aging and adrenocorticoids: quantitative correlations. *Science*, Vol. 202, No. 4372, pp. 1098-1102.

Langbein, J., Siebert, K., Nürnberg, G. (2009). On the use of an automated learning device by group-housed dwarf goats: Do goats seek cognitive challenges? *Applied Animal Behaviour Science*, Vol. 120, No. 3–4, pp. 150-158.

Langenhof, M.R. and Komdeur, J. (2018). Why and how the early-life environment affects development of coping behaviors. *Behavioral Ecology and Sociobiology*, Vol. 72, p. 34.

Laryea, G., Arnett, M. G., Muglia, L.J. (2012). Behavioral studies and genetic alterations in Corticotropin-releasing hormone (CRH) neurocircuitry: Insights into human psychiatric disorders. *Behavioral Sciences (Basel, Switzerland),* Vol. 2, No. 2, pp. 135–171.

Laurence, N.C., Labuschagne, L.G., Lura, B.G. et al. (2015). Regular Exercise Enhances Task-Based Industriousness in Laboratory Rats. *PLoS ONE,* Vol. 10, No. 6, e0129831.

Lee, M. and Soya, H. (2017). Effects of acute voluntary loaded wheel running on BDNF expression in the rat hippocampus. *Journal of Exercise, Nutrition and Biochemistry*, Vol. 21, No. 4, pp. 52-57.

Lee, P. R., Brady, D.L. et al. (2007). Prenatal stress generates deficits in rat social behavior. *Brain Research*, Vol. 1156, pp. 152–167.

Lemaire, V., Koehl, M. et al. (2000). Prenatal stress produces learning deficits associated with an inhibition of neurogenesis in the hippocampus. *PNAS*, Vol. 97, No. 20, pp. 11032–11037.

Levine, S. and Wiener, S.G. (1988). Psychoendocrine aspects of mother-infant relationships in nonhuman primates. *Psychoneuroendocrinology*, Vol. 13, No. 1-2, pp. 143-154.

Lit, L., Boehm, D., Marzke, S. et al. (2010). Certification testing as an acute naturalistic stressor for disaster dog handlers. *Stress,* Vol. 13, No. 5, pp. 392-401.

Liu, D., Diorio, J., Tannenbaum, B. et al. (1997). Maternal Care, Hippocampal Glucocorticoid Receptors, and Hypothalamic-Pituitary-Adrenal Responses to Stress. *Science*, Vol. 277, No. 5332, pp. 1659-1662.

Lo Iacono, L. and Carola, V. (2018). The impact of adolescent stress experiences on neurobiological development. *Seminars in Cell & Developmental Biology*, Vol. 77, pp. 93-103.

Long, V.A. and. Fanselow, M.S. (2012). Stress-enhanced fear learning in rats is resistant to the effects of immediate massed extinction. *Stress*, Vol. 15, No. 6, pp. 627-636.

Lucas, M., Ilin, Y., Anunu, R. et al. (2014). Long-term effects of controllability or the lack of it on coping abilities and stress resilience in the rat. *Stress*, Vol. 17, No. 5, pp. 423-430.

Lupien, S.J., McEwen, B.S. et al. (2009). Effects of stress throughout the lifespan on the brain, behaviour and cognition. *Nature Reviews Neuroscience,* Vol. 10, pp. 434-445.

Lukkes, J.L., Mokin, M.V., Scholl, J.L. et al. (2009). Adult rats exposed to early-life social isolation exhibit increased anxiety and conditioned fear behavior and altered hormonal stress responses. *Hormones and Behavior*, Vol. 55, pp. 248-256.

Luo, Y., Kuang, S., Xue, L. et al. The mechanism of 5-lipoxygenase in the impairment of learning and memory in rats subjected to chronic unpredictable mild stress. *Physiology & Behavior*, Vol. 167, pp. 145–153.

Lyons, D., Parker, K.J., Katz, M. (2009). Developmental cascades linking stress inoculation, arousal regulation, and resilience. *Frontiers in Behavioral Neuroscience*, Vol. 3, p. 32.

Lyons, D., Price, E.O., Moberg, G.P. Social modulation of pituitary-adrenal responsiveness and individual differences in behavior of young domestic goats. *Physiology & Behavior*, Vol. 43, No. 4, pp. 451-458.

Machado, C.J., Whitaker, A.M. et al. (2015). Maternal immune activation in nonhuman primates alters social attention in juvenile offspring. *Biological Psychiatry*, Vol. 77, No. 9, pp. 823–832.

Maier, S.F. (2015). Behavioral control blunts reactions to contemporaneous and future adverse events: Medial prefrontal cortex plasticity and a corticostriatal network. *Neurobiology of Stress*, Vol. 1, pp. 12-22.

Maier, S.F. and Watkins, L.R. (2005). Stressor controllability and learned helplessness: the roles of the dorsal raphe nucleus, serotonin, and corticotropin-releasing factor. *Neuroscience and Biobehavioral Reviews*, Vol. 29 No. 4-5, pp. 829-841.

Maier, S.F. and Seligman, M.E.P. (2016). Learned helplessness at fifty: insights from neuroscience. *Psychological Review*, Vol. 123, No. 4, pp. 349-367.

Maren, S. (2011). Seeking a Spotless Mind: Extinction, Deconsolidation, and Erasure of Fear Memory. *Neuron*, Vol. 70, No. 5, pp. 830-845.

Maren, S. and Chang. C.H. (2006). Recent fear is resistant to extinction. *PNAS*, Vol.103, No. 47, pp. 18020–18025.

Maren, S. and. Holmes, A. (2016). Stress and fear extinction. *Neuropscyhopharmacology*, Vol. 41, pp. 58-79.

Mason, W.A. (1960). The effects of social restriction on the behavior of rhesus monkeys: I. Free social behavior. *Journal of Comparative and Physiological Psychology*, Vol. 53, No. 6, pp. 582-589.

Mason, G.J. (1991). Stereotypies: a critical review. *Animal Behaviour*, Vol. 41, No. 6, pp. 1015-1037.

Mason, G., Clubb, R., Latham, N. et al. (2007). Why and how should we use environmental enrichment to tackle stereotypic behaviour? *Applied Animal Behaviour Science*, Vol. 102, No. 3-4, pp. 163–188.

Matheson, S.M., Asher, L., Bateson, M. (2008). Larger, enriched cages are associated with 'optimistic' response biases in captive European starlings (Sturnus vulgaris). *Applied Animal Behaviour Science*, Vol. 109, pp. 374-383.

Maul, S., Giegling, I., Fabbri, C. et al. (2020). Genetics of resilience: Implications from genome-wide association studies and candidate genes of the stress response system in posttraumatic stress disorder and depression, *American Journal of Medical Genetics*, Vol. 183B, pp. 77-94.

McCormick, C. M. and Mathews, I.Z. (2007). HPA function in adolescence: role of sex hormones in its regulation and the enduring consequences of exposure to stressors. *Pharmacology Biochemistry and Behavior*, Vol. 86, No. 2, pp. 220–233.

McCullough, A., Ruehrdanz, A., Jenkins, M.A. et al. (2018). Measuring the effects of an animal-assisted intervention for pediatric oncology patients and their parents: a multisite randomized controlled trial. *Journal of Pediatric Oncology Nursing*, Vol. 35, No. 3, pp. 159-177.

McEwen, Bruce S. (2017). Neurobiological and systemic effects of chronic stress. *Chronic stress (Thousand Oaks, Calif.), 1*, 2470547017692328.

McEwen, B.S., Gray, J.D., Nasca, C. (2015). Recognizing resilience: Learning from the effects of stress on the brain. *Neurobiology of Stress*, Vol. 1, pp. 1-11.

McEwen B.S. and Mirsky, A.E. (2018). From serendipity to clinical relevance: How clinical psychology and neuroscience converged to illuminate psychoneuroendocrinology. *Psychoneuroendocrinology*, Vol. 105, DOI: 10.1016/j.psyneuen.2018.09.011

McEwen, B.S. and Stella, E. (1993). Stress and the individual. Mechanisms leading to disease. *Archives of Internal Medicine*, Vol. 153, pp. 2093-2101.

McGarry, S., Girdler, S., McDonald, A. et al. (2013). Paediatric health-care professionals: Relationships between psychological distress, resilience and coping skills. *Journal of Pediatrics and Child Health*, Vol. 49, No. 9, pp. 725-732.

McGowan, R.T.S., Bolte, C., Barnett, H.R. et al. (2018). Can you spare 15 min? The measurable positive impact of a 15-min petting session on shelter dog well-being. *Applied Animal Behaviour Science*, Vol. 203, pp. 42-54.

McGowan, R.T.S., Rehn, T., Norling, Y. et al. (2014). Positive affect and learning: exploring the "Eureka Effect" in dogs. *Animal Cognition*, Vol. 17, pp. 577-587.

McGuire, J., Herman, J.P., Horn, P.S. et al. (2010). Enhanced fear recall and emotional arousal in rats recovering from chronic variable stress. *Physiology & Behavior*, Vol. 101, No. 4, pp. 474-482.

McMillan, F.D. (2020). Psychological Trauma and Posttraumatic Psychopathology in Animals. In F.D. McMillan (Ed.), Mental Health and Well-being in Animals, 2nd ed., pp. 182-211. CABI.

Mastorakos, G., Pavlatou, M., Diamanti-Kandarakis, E. et al. (2005). Exercise and the stress system. *Homones (Athens)*, Vol. 4, No. 2, pp. 73-89.

Meaney, M.J. and Szyf, M. (2005). Environmental programming of stress responses through DNA methylation: life at the interface between a dynamic environment and a fixed genome. *Dialogues in Clinical Neuroscience*, Vol. 7, No. 2, pp. 103-123.

Mech, L.D. (1999). Alpha status, dominance, and division of labor in wolf packs. *Canadian Journal of Zoology*, Vol. 77, pp. 1196-1203.

Meehan, C.L. and Mench, J.A. (2007). The challenge of challenge: Can problem solving opportunities enhance animal welfare? *Applied Animal Behaviour Science*, Vol. 102, No. 304, pp. 246–261.

Meewisse, M., Reitsma, J.B. et al. (2007). Cortisol and post-traumatic stress disorder in adults. *British Journal of Psychiatry*, Vol. 191, pp. 387-392.

Mellen, J. and Sevenich MacPhee, M. (2001). Philosophy of environmental enrichment: past, present, and future, *Zoo Biology*, Vol. 20, No. 3, pp. 211–226.

Mendl, M., Brooks, J., Basse, C. et al. (2010). Dogs showing separation-related behaviour exhibit a 'pessimistic' cognitive bias. *Current Biology*, Vol. 20, No. 19, pp. R839-R840.

Merz, C.J., Wolf, O.T., Hennig, J. (2010). Stress impairs retrieval of socially relevant information. *Behavioral Neuroscience*, Vol. 124, No. 2, pp. 288-293.

Meyer, J. S. (1983). Early adrenalectomy stimulates subsequent growth and development of the rat brain. *Experimental Neurology*, Vol. 82, No. 2, pp. 432–436.

Milgram, N.W., Head, E., Zicker, S.C. et al. (2005). Learning ability in aged beagle dogs is preserved by behavioral enrichment and dietary fortification: a two-year longitudinal study. *Neurobiology of Aging*, Vol. 26, No. 1, pp. 77-90.

Miller, R.M., Marriott, D., Trotter, J. et al. (2018). Running exercise mitigates the negative consequences of chronic stress on dorsal hippocampal long-term potentiation in male mice. *Neurobiology of Learning and Memory*, Vol. 149, pp. 28-38.

Mikkola, S., Salonen, M., Pureness, J. et al. (2021). Aggressive behaviour is affected by demographic, environmental and behavioral factors in purebred dogs. *Scientific Reports*, Vol. 11, p. 9433.

Mineka, S., Gunnar, M., Champoux, M. (1986). Control and early socioemotional development: infant rhesus monkeys reared in controllable versus uncontrollable environments. *Child Development*, Vol. 57, No. 5, pp. 1241-1256.

Miracle, A.D., Brace, M.F., Huyck, K.D. (2006). Chronic stress impairs recall of extinction of conditioned fear. Neurobiology of Learning and Memory, Vol. 85, No. 3, pp. 213–218.

Molet, J., Maras, P.M., Avishai-Eliner, S. et al. (2014). Naturalistic rodent models of chronic early-life stress. *Developmental Psychobiology*, Vol. 56, No. 8, pp. 1675–1688.

Moon, L.E. and Lodahl, T.M. (1956). The Reinforcing Effect of Changes in Illumination on Lever-Pressing in the Monkey. *The American Journal of Psychology*, Vol. 69, No. 2, pp. 260-288.

Morley-Fletcher, S., Darnaudery, M. et al. (2003). Prenatal stress in rats predicts immobility behavior in the forced swim test. Effects of a chronic treatment with tianeptine. *Brain Research*, Vol. 989, No. 2, pp. 246–251.

Moscarello, J.M. and Hartley, C.A. (2017). Agency and the calibration of motivated behavior. *Trends in Cognitive Sciences* Vol. 21, No. 10, pp. 725-735.

Mumtaz, F., Khan, M.I., Zubair, M. et al. (2018). Neurobiology and consequences of social isolation stress in animal model—A comprehensive review. *Biomedicine & Pharmacotherapy*, Vol. 105, pp. 1205-1222.

Murínová, J., Hlaváčová, N., Chmelová, M. et al. (2017). The Evidence for Altered BDNF Expression in the Brain of Rats Reared or Housed in Social Isolation: A Systematic Review. *Frontiers in Behavioral Neuroscience*, Vol. 11, p. 101.

Nakamura, J. and Csikszentmihalyi, M. (2002). The concept of Flow. Handbook of Positive Psychology, pp. 89-105.

National Clearinghouse on Child Abuse and Neglect. (2005). Long-term Consequences of Child Abuse and Neglect. U.S. Department of Health and Human Services.

Nazeri, M., Shabani, M. et al. (2015). Psychological or physical prenatal stress differentially affects cognition behaviors. *Physiology & Behavior*, Vol. 142, pp. 155–60.

Nederhof, E. and Schmidt, M.V. (2012). Mismatch or cumulative stress: Toward an integrated hypothesis of programming effects. *Physiology & Behavior*, Vol. 106, No. 5, pp. 691-700.

Nickels, N., Kubicki, K., Maestripieri, D. (2017). Sex differences in the effects of psychosocial stress on cooperative and prosocial behavior: evidence for 'flight or fight' in males and 'tend and befriend' in females. *Adaptive Human Behavior and Physiology*, Vol. 3, pp. 171-182.

Oesterwind, S., Nürnberg, G., Puppe, B. et al. (2016). Impact of structural and cognitive enrichment on the learning performance, behavior and physiology of dwarf goats (Capra aegagrus hircus). *Applied Animal Behaviour Science*, Vol. 177, pp. 34-41.

Ogrizek, M. et al. (2018). Injections to pregnant mice produce prenatal stress that affects aggressive behavior in their adult male offspring. *Hormones and Behavior*, Vol. 106, pp. 35–43.

Olsson, I.A.S. and Dahlborn, K. (2002). Improving housing conditions for laboratory mice: a review of "environmental enrichment." *Laboratory Animals*, Vol. 36, No. 3, pp. 243–270.

Osório, C., Probert, T., Jones, E. et al. (2016). Adapting to stress: Understanding the neurobiology of resilience, *Behavioral Medicine (Washington D.C.)*, Vol. 43, No. 4, pp. 307-322.

Overmier J.B. and Seligman, M.E. (1967). Effects of inescapable shock upon subsequent escape and avoidance responding. *Journal of Comparative and Physiological Psychology*. Vol. 63, No. 1, pp. 28–33.

Padgett, D. A., Marucha, P. T. et al. (1998). Restraint stress slows cutaneous wound healing in mice. *Brain, Behavior and Immunology*, Vol. 12, pp. 64–73.

Papaioannou, A., Gerozissis, K., Prokopiou, A., et al. (2002). Sex differences in the effects of neonatal handling on the animal's response to stress and the vulnerability of depressive behaviour. *Behavioral Brain Research*, Vol. 129, No. 1-2, pp. 131-139.

Paredes, D. and Morilak, D.A. (2019). A Rodent Model of Exposure Therapy: The Use of Fear Extinction as a Therapeutic Intervention for PTSD. *Frontiers in Behavioral Neuroscience*, Vol. 13, p. 46.

Park, M.K., Hoang, T.A., Belluzzi, J.D. et al. (2003). Gender specific effect of neonatal handling on stress reactivity in adolescent rats. *Journal of Neuroendocrinology*, Vol. 15, No. 3, pp. 286-295.

Parker, K.J., Buckmaster, C.L., Justus, K.R. et al. (2005). Mild early life stress enhances prefrontal-dependent response inhibition in monkeys. *Biological Psychiatry*, Vol. 57, No. 8, pp. 848-855.

Parker, K.J., Buckmaster C.L., Schatzberg A.F. et al. (2004). Prospective investigation of stress inoculation in young monkeys. *Archive of General Psychiatry*. Vol. 61, No. 9, pp. 933–941.

Parker, K.J. and Maestripieri, D. (2011). Identifying key features of early stressful experiences that produce stress vulnerability and resilience in primates. *Neuroscience and Biobehavioral Reviews*, Vol. 35, pp. 1466-1483.

Parker, K. J., Rainwater, K. L., Buckmaster, C. L. et al. (2007). Early life stress and novelty seeking behavior in adolescent monkeys. *Psychoneuroendocrinology*, Vol. 32, No. 7, pp. 785–792.

Pastore, C., Pirrone, F., Balzarotti, F. et al. (2011). Evaluation of physiological and behavioral stress-dependent parameters in agility dogs. *Journal of Veterinary Behavior*, Vol. 6, No. 3, pp. 188-194.

Patin, V., Lordi, A. et al. (2005). Effects of prenatal stress on anxiety and social interactions in adult rats. *Developmental Brain Research*, Vol. 160, No. 2, pp. 265–274.

Pattwell, S.S., Duhoux, S., Hartley, C.A. et al. (2012). Altered fear learning across development in both mouse and human. *PNAS*, Vol. 109, No. 40, pp. 16318–16323.

Pavlov, I. P. (1927). Conditioned reflexes: an investigation of the physiological activity of the cerebral cortex. Oxford University Press.

Payne, J.D., Jackson, E.D., Ryan, L. et al. (2006). The impact of stress on neutral and emotional aspects of episodic memory. Memory, Vol. 14, No. 1, pp. 1–16.

Pellis, S.M. and Pellis, V.C. (2007). Rough and tumble play and the development of the social brain. *Current Directions in Psychological Science*, Vol. 16, No. 2, pp. 95–98.

Pellis, S.M., Pellis, V.C., Bell, H.C. (2010). The function of play in the development of the social brain. *American Journal of Play*, Vol. 2, No. 3, pp. 278–296.

Pierantoni, L., Albertini, M., Pirrone, F. (2011). Prevalence of owner-reported behaviours in dogs separated from the litter at two different ages. *Veterinary Record,* Vol. 169, p. 468.

Plotsky, P.M., Ladd, C.O., Huot, R.L. et al. (1997). Long-term consequences of maternal separation in Long Evans rats and their reversal by antidepressants. *Psychoneuroendocrinology*, Vol. 22 (Supp. 2), p. S174.

Preuss, D. and Wolf, O. T. (2009). Post-learning psychosocial stress enhances consolidation of neutral stimuli. *Neurobiology of Learning and Memory*, Vol. 92, No. 3, pp. 318–326.

Protopopova, Alexandra. (2016). Effects of sheltering on physiology, immune function, behavior, and the welfare of dogs. *Physiology & Behavior*, Vol. 159, pp. 95-103.

Puppe, B., Ernst, K., Schön, P.C. et al. (2007). Cognitive enrichment affects behavioural reactivity in domestic pigs. *Applied Animal Behaviour Science*, Vol. 105, No. 1–3, pp. 75-86.

Puurunen, J., Hakanen, E., Salonen, M.K. et al. (2020). Inadequate socialisation, inactivity, and urban living environment are associated with social fearfulness in pet dogs. *Scientific Reports*, Vol. 10, 3527.

Rau, V., DeCola, J.P., Fanselow M.S. (2005). Stress-induced enhancement of fear learning: An animal model of posttraumatic stress disorder. *Neuroscience & Biobehavioral Reviews*, Vol. 29, No. 8, pp. 1207-1223.

Rault, J. (2012). Friends with benefits: Social support and its relevance for farm animal welfare. *Applied Animal Behavior Science*, Vol. 136, pp. 1-14.

Rayen, I., van den Hove, D.L. et al. (2011). Fluoxetine during development reverses the effects of prenatal stress on depressive-like behavior and hippocampal neurogenesis in adolescence. *PLoS ONE*, Vol. 6, No. 9, e24003.

Rodgers, A.B., Morgan, C.P., Bronson, S.L. et al. (2013). Paternal stress exposure alters sperm microRNA content and reprograms offspring hpa stress axis regulation. *Journal of Neuroscience*, Vol. 33, No. 21, pp. 9003-9012.

Romeo, R.D. (2015). Perspectives on stress resilience and adolescent neurobehavioral function. *Neurobiology of Stress*, Vol. 1, pp. 128-133.

Romeo, R.D., Bellani, R., Karatsoreos, I.N. et al. (2006). Stress History and Pubertal Development Interact to Shape Hypothalamic-Pituitary-Adrenal Axis Plasticity. *Endocrinology*, Vol. 147, No. 4, pp. 1664-1674.

Roozendaal, B., Bohus, B. and McGaugh J.L. (1996). Dose-dependent suppression of adrenocortical activity with metyrapone: effects on emotion and memory. *Psychoneuroendocrinology*, Vol. 21, No. 8, pp. 681–693.

Rosenblum, L. A., Smith, E.L.P. et al. (2002). Differing concentrations of corticotropin-releasing factor and oxytocin in the cerebrospinal fluid of bonnet and pigtail macaques. *Psychoneuroendocrinology*, Vol. 27, pp. 651–660.

Roth, D. A., Coles, M.E. et al. (2002). The relationship between memories for childhood teasing and anxiety and depression in adulthood. *Journal of Anxiety Disorders*, Vol. 16, No. 2, pp. 149–164.

Ruis, M.A.W., Brake, J.H.A., Buwalda, B. et al. (1999). Housing familiar male wildtype rats together reduces the long-term adverse behavioural and physiological effects of social defeat. *Psychoneuroendocrinology*, Vol. 24, No. 3, pp. 285-300.

Russo-Neustadt, A., Ha, T., Ramirez, R. et al. (2001). Physical activity-antidepressant treatment combination: impact on brain-derived neurotrophic factor and behavior in an animal model. *Behavioural Brain Research*, Vol. 120, No. 1, pp. 87–95.

Rutten, B.P.F., Hammels, C., Geschwind, N. et al. (2013). Resilience in mental health: linking psychological and neurobiological perspectives. *Acta Psychiatrica Scandinavia*, Vol. 128, No. 1, pp. 3–20.

Špinka, M. and Wemelsfelder, F. (2011). Environmental Challenge and Animal Agency. *Animal Welfare*, Wallingford, Uk: CAB International, pp. 27-44.

Sands, J. and Creel, S. Social dominance, aggression and faecal glucocorticoid levels in a wild population of wolves, Canis lupus, *Animal Behaviour*, Vol. 67, No. 3, pp. 387-396.

Salmon P. (2001). Effects of physical exercise on anxiety, depression, and sensitivity to stress: a unifying theory. Clinical Psychology Review, Vol. 21, No. 1, pp. 33–61.

Sambrook, T.D. and Buchanan-Smith, H.M. (1997). Control and complexity in novel object enrichment. *Animal Welfare*, Vol. 6, No. 3, pp. 207–216.

Sandi, C. and Haller, J. (2015). Stress and the social brain: behavioural effects and neurobiological mechanisms. *Nature Reviews Neuroscience*, Vol. 16, pp. 290-304.

Sandi, C., Loscertales, M., Guaza, C. (1997). Experience-dependent facilitating effect of corticosterone on spatial memory formation in the water maze. *European Journal of Neuroscience*, Vol. 9, No. 4, pp. 637-642.

Sánchez, M.M., Ladd, C.O. et al. (2001). Early adverse experience as a developmental risk factor for later psychopathology: evidence from rodent and primate models. *Development and Psychopathology*, Vol. 13, No. 3, pp. 419-449.

Sánchez, M.M., Noble P.M. et al. (2005). Alterations in diurnal cortisol rhythm and acoustic startle response in nonhuman primates with adverse rearing. *Biological Psychiatry*, Vol. 57, pp. 373–381.

Schayek, R. and Maroun, M. (2014). Differences in stress-induced changes in extinction and prefrontal plasticity in post weanling and adult animals. *Biological Psychiatry*, Vol. 78, No. 3, pp. 159-166.

Schiele, M.A. and Domschke, K. (2018). Epigenetics at the crossroads between genes, environment and resilience in anxiety disorders. *Genes, Brain and Behavior*, Vol. 17, pp. 1-15.

Schilder, M. B. H., and van der Borg, J.A.M. (2004). Training dogs with help of the shock collar: Short and long term behavioural effects. *Applied Animal Behaviour Science*, Vol. 85, No. 3-4, pp. 319–334.

Schilder, M.B.H., Vinke, C.M. et al. (2014). Dominance in domestic dogs revisited: Useful habit and useful construct? *Journal of Veterinary Behavior*, Vol. 9, pp. 184-191.

Schmeltzer, S.N., Vollmer, L.L., Rush, J.E. et al. (2015). History of chronic stress modifies acute stress-evoked fear memory and acoustic startle in male rats. *The International Journal on the Biology of Stress*, Vol. 18, No. 2, pp. 244-253.

Schneider, M. L. and Coe, C. L. (1993). Repeated social stress during pregnancy impairs neuromotor development of the primate infant. *Journal of Developmental and Behavioral Pediatrics*, Vol. 14, No. 2, pp. 81–87.

Schöberl, I., Beetz, A., Solomon, J. et al. (2016). Social factors influencing cortisol modulation in dogs during a strange situation procedure. *Journal of Veterinary Behavior*, Vol. 11, pp. 77-85.

Schöberl, I., Wedl, M., Bauer, B. et al. (2012). Effects of owner–dog relationship and owner personality on cortisol modulation in human–dog dyads. *Anthrozoös*, Vol. 25, pp. 199-214.

Schöner, J., Heinz, A. et al. (2017). Post-traumatic stress disorder and beyond: an overview of rodent stress models. *Journal of Cellular and Molecular Medicine*, Vol. 21, No. 10, pp. 2248-2256.

Schulkin, J. (2003). Allostasis: a neural behavioral perspective. *Hormones and Behavior*, Vol.43, pp. 21-27.

Schulkin, J., Gold, P.W., McEwen, B.S. (1998). Induction of corticotropin-releasing hormone gene expression by glucocorticoids: implication for understanding the states of fear and anxiety and allostatic load. *Psychoneuroendocrinology*, Vol. 23, No. 3, pp. 219-243.

Schwabe, L., Oitzl, M.S. et al. (2007). Stress modulates the use of spatial versus stimulus-response learning strategies in humans, *Learning & Memory*, Vol. 14, pp. 109-116.

Schwabe, L. and Wolf, O.T. (2009). Stress prompts habit behavior in humans. *Journal of Neuroscience,* Vol. 29, pp. 7191–7198.

Schwabe, L. and Wolf, O.T. (2010). Learning under stress impairs memory formation. *Neurobiology of Learning and Memory*, Vol. 93, pp. 183-188.

Schwabe, L., Wolf, O.T, Oitzl, M.S. (2010). Memory formation under stress: Quantity and quality. *Neuroscience and Biobehavioral Reviews*, Vol. 34, pp. 584-591.

Seckl, J.R. (2008). Glucocorticoids, developmental 'programming' and the risk of affective dysfunction. *Progress in Brain Research*, Vol. 167, pp. 17-34.

Secoli, S. R. and Teixeira, N.A. (1998). Chronic prenatal stress affects development and behavioral depression in rats. *Stress*, Vol. 2, No. 4, pp. 273–280.

Seeman, E., Singer, B.H. et al. (1997). Price of adaptation—allostatic load and its health consequences. *Archives of Internal Medicine*, vol. 157, pp. 2259-2268.

Seeman, T.E., McEwen, B.S. et al. (2001). Allostatic load as a marker of cumulative biological risk: MacArthur studies of successful aging. *PNAS*, Vol. 98, No. 8, pp. 4770-4775.

Selye, H. (1950). Stress and the general adaptation syndrome. *British Medical Journal,* pp. 1383-1392.

Shettleworth, S.J. (2010.) Cognition, Evolution and Behavior. Oxford University Press, Oxford UK.

Shields, G.S., Sazma, M.A., McCullough, A.M. et al. (2017). The effects of acute stress on episodic memory: a meta-analysis and integrative review. *Psychological Bulletin*, Vol. 143, No. 6, pp. 636-675.

Shiverdecker, M.D., Schiml, P.S., Hennessy, M.B. (2013). Human interaction moderates plasma cortisol and behavioral responses of dogs to shelter housing. *Physiology & Behavior*, Vol. 109, pp. 75-79.

Shumake, J., Ferguson-Moreira, S., Monfils, M.H. (2014). Predictability and heritability of individual differences in fear learning. *Animal Cognition*, Vol. 17, pp. 1207–1221.

Siegel, S.J., Ginsberg, S.D., Hof, P.R. et al. (1993). Effects of social deprivation in prepubescent rhesus monkeys: immunohistochemical analysis of the neurofilament protein triplet in the hippocampal formation. *Brain Research*, Vol. 619, No. 1-2, pp. 299-305.

Siever, L.J. (2008). Neurobiology of Aggression and Violence. *The American Journal of Psychiatry*, Vol. 165, No. 4, pp. 429-442.

Sih, A. (2011). Effects of early stress on behavioral syndromes: An integrated adaptive perspective. *Neuroscience and Biobehavioral Reviews,* Vol. 35, pp. 1452-1465.

Singewald, N. and Holmes, A. (2019). Rodent models of impaired fear extinction. *Psychopharmacology*, Vol. 236, pp. 21–32.

Slabbert J.M., Rasa O.A. (1993). The effect of early separation from the mother on pups in bonding to humans and pup health. *Journal of the South African Veterinary Association.*, Vol. 64, No. 1, pp. 4-8.

Smith, A.S. and Wang, Z. (2014). Hypothalamic oxytocin mediates social buffering of the stress response. *Biological Psychiatry*, Vol. 76, No. 4, pp. 281-288.

Squire, L.R. and Zola, S.M. (1996). Structure and function of declarative and nondeclarative memory systems. *PNAS*, Vol. 93, No. 24, pp. 13515–13522.

Southwick, S.M. and Charney, D.S. (2012). The science of resilience: Implications for the prevention and treatment of depression. *Science*, Vol. 338, No. 6103, pp. 79–82.

Stanton, M.E., Gutierrez, Y.R., Levine, S. (1998). Maternal deprivation potentiaties pituitary-adrenal stress responses in infant rats. *Behavioral Neuroscience*, Vol. 102, pp. 692-700.

Sterling, P. (2004). Principles of allostasis: Optimal design, predictive regulation, pathophysiology, and rational therapeutics. In J. Schulkin (Ed.), *Allostasis, homeostasis, and the costs of physiological adaptation* (pp. 17–64). Cambridge University Press.

Sterling P. and Eyer, J. (1988). Allostasis: A New Paradigm to Explain Arousal Pathology in *Handbook of Life Stress, Cognition and Health,* ed. S Fisher, J Reason, pp. 629-49. New York: John Wiley & Sons.

Stranahan, A.M., Lee, K., Mattson, M.P. (2008). Central mechanisms of HPA axis regulation by voluntary exercise. *Neuromolecular Medicine*, Vol. 10, No. 2, pp. 118-127.

Sundman, A., Van Poucke, E. et al. (2019). Long-term stress levels are synchronized in dogs and their owners. *Scientific Reports*, Vol. 9, 7391.

Suo, L., Zhao, L., Si, J. et al. (2013). Predictable chronic mild stress in adolescence increases resilience in adulthood. *Neuropsychopharmacology*, Vol. 38, No. 8, pp. 1387–1400.

Takahashi, L.K., Haglin, C. et al. (1992). Prenatal stress potentiates stress-induced behavior and reduces the propensity to play in juvenile rats. *Physiology & Behavior*, Vol. 51, No. 2, pp. 319–323.

Taylor, G.T. (1981). Fear and affiliation in domesticated male rats. *Journal of Comparative and Physiological Psychology*, Vol. 95, No. 5, pp. 685–693.

Taylor, S. E., Klein, L. C., Lewis, B. P. et al. (2000). Biobehavioral responses to stress in females: Tend-and-befriend, not fight-or-flight. *Psychological Review*, Vol. 107, No. 3, pp. 411–429.

Tiira, K. (2019). Resilience in dogs? Lessons from other species. *Veterinary Medicine (Auckland, N.Z.)*, Vol. 10, pp. 159-168.

Tiira, K. and Lohi, H. (2015). Early life experiences and exercise associate with canine anxieties. *PLoS One*, Vol. 10, No. 11, e0141907.

Titulaer, M., Blackwell, E.J., Mendl, M. et al. (2013). Cross sectional study comparing behavioural, cognitive and physiological indicators of welfare between short and long term kennelled domestic dogs. *Applied Animal Behaviour Science*, Vol. 147, No. 1-2, pp. 149-158.

Toates, F. (2004). Cognition, motivation, emotion and action: a dynamic and vulnerable interdependence. *Applied Animal Behaviour Science*, Vol. 86, No. 304, pp. 173-204.

Tsoory, M., Cohen, H., Richter-Levin, G. (2007). Juvenile stress induces a predisposition to either anxiety or depressive-like symptoms following stress in adulthood. *European Neuropsychopharmacology*, Vol. 17, No. 4, pp. 245-256.

Valenchon, M., Lévy, F., Prunier, A. et al. (2013). Stress Modulates Instrumental Learning Performances in Horses (Equus caballus) in Interaction with Temperament. *PLoS One*, Vol. 8, No. 4, e62324.

Valentin, V.V., Dickinson, A., O'Doherty, J.P. (2007). Determining the neural substrates of goal-directed learning in the human brain. *The Journal of Neuroscience*, Vol. 27, No. 15, pp. 4019–4026.

Vallée, M., Mayo, W. et al. (1997). Prenatal stress induces high anxiety and postnatal handling induces low anxiety in adult offspring: correlation with stress-induced corticosterone secretion. *The Journal of Neuroscience*, Vol. 17, No. 7, pp. 2626–2636.

Van den Bergh, B. R. H., Van Calster, B. et al. (2008). Antenatal maternal anxiety is related to HPA-axis dysregulation and self-reported depressive symptoms in adolescence: a prospective study on the fetal origins of depressed mood. *Neuropsychopharmacology*, Vol. 33, No. 3, pp. 536–545.

van der Kooij, M.A., Fantin, M. et al. (2014). Impaired hippocampal neuroligin-2 function by chronic stress or synthetic peptide treatment is linked to social deficits and increased aggression, *Neuropsychopharmacology*, Vol. 29, pp. 1148-1158.

Van Oers, H.J.J., de Kloet, E.R., Levine, S. (1998). Early vs. late maternal deprivation differentially alters the endocrine and hypothalamic responses to stress. *Developmental Brain Research*, Vol. 11, pp. 245-252.

Van Oers, H.J.J., de Kloet, E.R., Levine, S. (2001). Persistent Effects of Maternal Deprivation on HPA Regulation Can Be Reversed By Feeding and Stroking, But Not By Dexamethasone. Vol. 11, No. 8, pp. 581-588.

VanElzakker, M. B., Dahlgren, M. K., Davis, F. C., Dubois, S., Shin, L. M. (2014). From Pavlov to PTSD: the extinction of conditioned fear in rodents, humans, and anxiety disorders. Neurobiology of learning and memory, 113, pp. 3–18.

Vazquez, D.M. and Akil, H. (1993). Pituitary-adrenal response to ether vapor in the weanling animal: characterization of the inhibitory effect of the glucocorticoids on adrenocorticotropin secretion. *Pediatric Research*, Vol. 34, pp. 646-653.

Vecchio, L.M., Ying, M., Xhima, K. et al. (2018). The neuroprotective effects of exercise: Maintaining a healthy brain throughout aging. *Brain Plasticity*, Vol. 4, No. 1, pp. 17-52.

Veenema, A.H. (2009). Early life stress, the development of aggression and neuroendocrine and neurobiological correlates: what can we learn from animal models? *Frontiers in Neuroendocrinology*, Vol. 30, No. 4, pp. 497–518.

Veenema, A.H., Blume, A. et al. (2006). Effects of early life stress on adult male aggression and hypothalamic vasopressin and serotonin. *European Journal of Neuroscience*, Vol. 24, No. 6, pp. 1711–1720.

Von Frijtag, J.C., Schot, M., van den Bos, R. et al. (2002). Individual housing during the play period results in changed responses to and consequences of a psychosocial stress situation in rats. *Developmental Psychobiology*, Vol. 41, No. 1, pp. 58–69.

Walker, J.K., Dale, A.R., D'Eath, R.B. et al. (2016). Qualitative Behaviour Assessment of dogs in the shelter and home environment and relationship with quantitative behaviour assessment and physiological responses. *Applied Animal Behaviour Science*, Vol. 184, pp. 97-108.

Wang, Q., Timberlake, M.A. et al. (2017). The recent progress in animal models of depression. *Progress in Neuro-psychopharmacology & Biological Psychiatry*, Vol. 77, pp. 99-109.

Watson, S.L., Shively, C.A., Voytko, M.L. (1999). Can puzzle feeders be used as cognitive screening instruments? Differential performance of young and aged female monkeys on a puzzle feeder task. *American Journal of Primatology*, Vol. 49, No. 2, pp. 195–202.

Weinstock, M. (2008). The long-term behavioural consequences of prenatal stress. *Neuroscience & Biobehavioral Reviews*, Vol. 32, No. 6, pp. 1073–1086.

Westenbroek, C., Ter Horst, G.J., Roos, M.H. et al. (2003). Gender-specific effects of social housing in rats after chronic mild stress exposure. *Progress in Neuro-Psychopharmacology and Biological Psychiatry*, Vol. 27, No. 1, pp. 21-30.

Westlund, K. (2014). Training is enrichment—And beyond. *Applied Animal Behaviour Science*, Vol. 152, pp. 1-6.

White, S., Acierno, R., Ruggiero, K. J. et al. (2013). Association of CRHR1 variants and posttraumatic stress symptoms in hurricane exposed adults. *Journal of Anxiety Disorders*, Vol. 27, No. 7, pp. 678–683.

Wiegert, O., Joëls, M., Krugers, H. Timing is essential for rapid effects of corticosterone on synaptic potentiation in the mouse hippocampus. *Learning & Memory*, Vol. 13, No. 2, pp. 110-113.

Wiepkema, P.R. Abnormal behaviour in farm animals: ethological implications. *Netherlands Journal of Zoology*, Vol. 35, pp. 279-299.

Willner, P. (2005). Chronic mild stress (CMS) revisited: consistency and behavioural-neurobiological concordance in the effects of CMS. *Neuropsychobiology*, Vol. 52, No. 2, pp. 90–110.

Willner. P., Towell, A., Sampson, D. et al. (1987). Reduction of sucrose preference by chronic unpredictable mild stress, and its restoration by a tricyclic antidepressant. *Psychopharmacology*, Vol. 93, No. 3, pp. 358-364.

Wilson, C.A., Schade, R. et al. (2012). Variable prenatal stress results in impairments of sustained attention and inhibitory response control in a 5-choice serial reaction time task in rats. *Neuroscience*, Vol. 218, pp. 126-137.

Wilson, C.A., Vazdarjanova, A. et al. (2013). Exposure to variable prenatal stress in rats: effects on anxiety-related behaviors, innate and contextual fear, and fear extinction. *Behavioural Brain Research*, Vol. 238, pp. 279-288.

Wirz, L., Bogdanov, M., Schwabe, L. (2018). Habits under stress: mechanistic insights across different types of learning. *Current Opinion in Behavioral Sciences*, Vol. 20, pp. 9-16.

Wrann, C.D., White, J.P., Salogiannis, J. et al. (2013). Exercise induces Hippocampal BDNF through a PGC-1α/FNDC5 Pathway. *Cell Metabolism*, Vol. 18, No. 5, pp. 649–659.

Wojtaś, J., Karpiński, M., Czyżowski, P. (2020). Salivary Cortisol Interactions in Search and Rescue Dogs and Their Handlers. *Animals*, Vol. 10, No. 4, p. 595.

Wood, P.A., de Bie, J., Clarke, J.A. (2014). Behavioural and physiological responses of domestic dogs (*Canis familiaris*) to agonistic growls from conspecifics, *Applied Animal Behaviour Science*, Vol. 161, pp. 105–112.

Wood, S.K. and Bhatnagar, S. (2015). Resilience to the effects of social stress: Evidence from clinical and preclinical studies on the role of coping strategies. *Neurobiology of Stress*, Vol. 1, pp. 164-173.

Wood, S.K., Wood, C.S., Lombard, C.M. et al. (2015). Inflammatory factors mediate vulnerability to a social stress-induced depressive-like phenotype in passive coping rats. *Biological Psychiatry*, Vol. 78, pp. 38-48.

Woon, F.L., Sood, S., Hedges, D.W. (2010). Hippocampal volume deficits associated with exposure to psychological trauma and posttraumatic stress disorder in adults: A meta-analysis. *Progress in Neuro-Psychopharmacology and Biological Psychiatry*, Vol. 34, No. 7, pp. 1181-1188.

Wright, I.K., Upton, N., Marsden, C.A. (1991). Resocialisation of isolation-reared rats does not alter their anxiogenic profile on the elevated X-maze model of anxiety. *Physiology &Behavior*, Vol. 50, No. 6, pp. 1129–1132.

Yao, Y., Robinson, A.M., Zucchi, F.C. et al. (2014). Ancestral exposure to stress epigenetically programs preterm birth risk and adverse maternal and newborn outcomes. *BMC Medicine*, Vol. 12, p. 121.

Yates, J.R., Beckmann, J.S., Meyer, A.C. et al. (2013). Concurrent choice for social interaction and amphetamine using conditioned place preference in rats: effects of age and housing condition. *Drug and Alcohol Dependence*, Vol. 129, No. 3, pp. 240–246.

Zebunke, M., Puppe, B., Langbein, J. (2013). Effects of cognitive enrichment on behavioural and physiological reactions of pigs. *Physiology & Behavior*, Vol. 118, pp. 70-79.

Zimmer, C., Taff, C.C., Ardia, D.R. et al. (2018). On again, off again: Acute stress response and negative feedback together predict resilience to experimental challenges. *Functional Ecology*, Vol. 33, No. 4, pp. 619-628.

Zuj, D.V., Palmer, M.A., Lommen, M.J.J. et al. (2016). The centrality of fear extinction in linking risk factors to PTSD: A narrative review. *Neuroscience and Biobehavioral Reviews*, Vol. 69, pp. 15-35.

About the Author

Dr. Kristina Spaulding has always been fascinated by animal behavior. As a child, she spent hours observing animals and wondering how they experienced the world. She was equally captivated by science. These two interests led her to earn her undergraduate degree in Wildlife Ecology and, eventually, her PhD in biopsychology—the study of the biological basis of behavior. She has been in the dog training and behavior field since 1999 and she is a Certified Applied Animal Behaviorist. Dr. Spaulding is particularly interested in stress, neurobiology, cognition and emotion and how to apply these concepts to improving the emotional wellbeing of animals.

In addition to working with clients on the prevention and treatment of behavior issues, Dr. Spaulding has a passion for teaching. She offers a variety of online courses and webinars on the science of behavior through her website, www.sciencemattersllc.com. She regularly gives invited talks at conferences and on other learning platforms. She strongly believes that science education should be accessible for everyone and strives to empower others by helping them bring science into their work with animals. She is Vice President of the not-for-profit International Association of Animal Behavior Consultants Foundation. Through her work with the foundation, she is able to further promote education, science and equality in the animal behavior field. She is also a member of the Pet Professional Guild's Advocacy Panel and Fear Free's Advisory Group.

She lives in upstate New York near the foothills of the Adirondacks with her husband Brendan, her son, Alex, her beagle mix, Darwin, and her Australian shepherd, Finn. In her free time, she enjoys hiking with her dogs, cycling, photography, and reading.

A

B

C

D

E

F

G

T

V

W

Z

Also available from Dogwise Publishing

Go to dogwise.com for more books and ebooks

Selecting and Training Service Dogs

HOW TO SUCCEED IN PUBLIC ACCESS WORK

Jennifer Cattett

Watching a service dog and her handler working as a team in a busy public space is a thing of beauty. Not every dog has the temperament or genetic make-up to do service work, but with the proper reward-based training, many dogs can succeed in public areas. Jennifer prepares you and your dog to meet the standards of the Public Access Test developed by Assistance Dogs International.

Starve Cancer

FEED YOUR DOG

Jo Cowden, PhD and Connie McMillan, DVM

In this important book, the authors present a nutritional regimen that helps dogs diagnosed with cancer maintain their body weight while at the same time denying the cancer what it needs to grow. The recommendations in this book are not going to cure them, but it improves their quality of life and extends life expectancy.

Canine Enrichment for the Real World

MAKING IT A PART OF YOUR DOG'S DAILY LIFE

Allie Bender and Emily Strong

In the world of dogs, there is now more awareness than ever of the need to provide enrichment, especially in shelters. But what exactly is enrichment? The concept is pretty straightforward: learn what your dog's needs are, and then structure an environment and routine that allows them to engage in behaviors they find enriching, while offering them opportunities to perform their natural or instinctual behaviors.

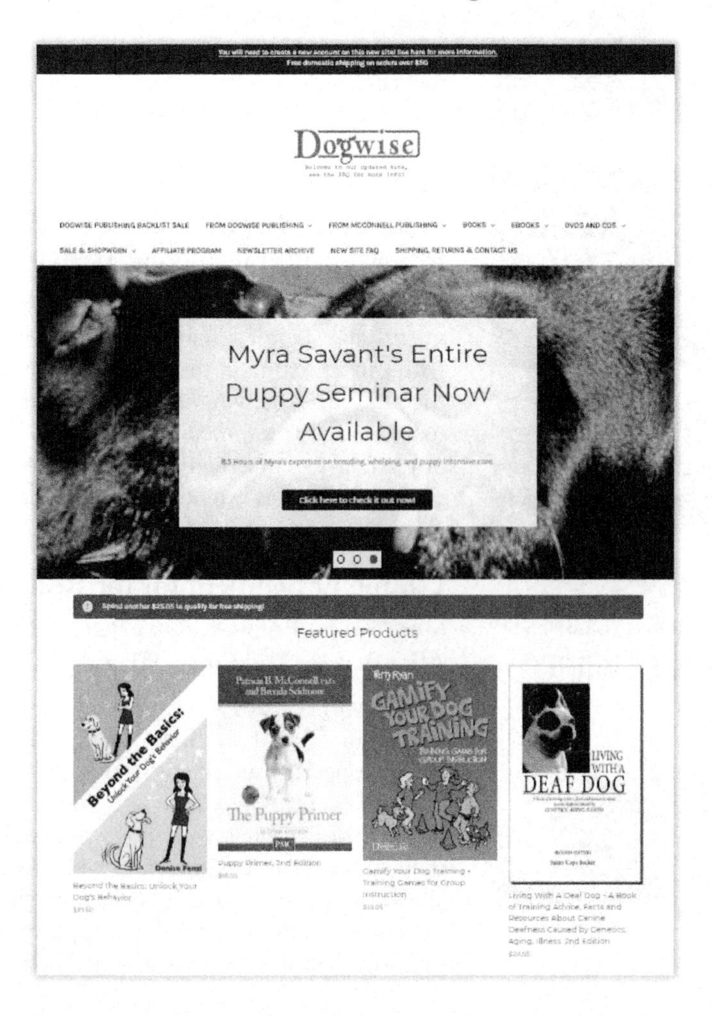
Dogwise
DOGWISE PUBLISHING BACKLIST SALE
FROM DOGWISE PUBLISHING
FROM MCCONNELL PUBLISHING
BOOKS
EBOOKS
DVDS AND CDS
SALE & SHOPWORN
AFFILIATE PROGRAM
NEWSLETTER ARCHIVE
NEW SITE FAQ
SHIPPING, RETURNS & CONTACT US
Myra Savant's Entire Puppy Seminar Now Available
Click here to check it out now!
Featured Products
Beyond the Basics: Unlock Your Dog's Behavior
Denise Fenzi
Patricia B. McConnell
Brenda Scidmore
The Puppy Primer
Terry Ryan
GAMIFY YOUR DOG TRAINING
LIVING WITH A DEAF DOG
Puppy Primer, 2nd Edition